D0908442

1200
6 50

PAUL A. AIKIN, Ph.D.
311 B Street
Davis, California 95616

Purchased from Moe's Used
Book Store 8/77

ANXIETY
and
Tension Control

ANXIETY

and
Tension Control

A Physiologic Approach

Edmund Jacobson, M.D., Ll.D., Ph.D., F.A.C.P.

Director, Laboratory for Clinical Physiology, Chicago, and the Jacobson Clinic; formerly Research Associate, Assistant Professor of Physiology (1926-1936), University of Chicago; Formerly Associate Attending Physician (Medicine), Michael Reese Hospital.

J. B. LIPPINCOTT COMPANY

PHILADELPHIA   MONTREAL

COPYRIGHT © 1964, BY EDMUND JACOBSON
    This book is fully protected by copyright and, with
    the exception of brief extracts for review, no part of
    it may be reproduced in any form without the writ-
    ten permission of the author.

Distributed in Great Britain by
Pitman Medical Publishing Co., Limited, London

Library of Congress Catalog Card Number 64-19018

Printed in The United States of America

To Harvey Kaplan,
In long friendship

Preface

Anxiety is excitation of the cerebrospinal as well as the autonomic nervous system when a menace is recognized or imagined and efforts are made to meet or avoid it. Smooth and striated muscle tension patterns with heightened action-potential levels mark the emotional reaction in which virtually the whole organism participates. This is the anxiety tension, the universal experience. Regulation, the avoidance of excessive tension, can be mediated through the striated (voluntary) musculature. When this musculature acts, as in effort-patterns, the function can be measured electrically; when this musculature relaxes toward zero levels, anxiety decreases during this diminution. In this sense, anxiety tension is a dependent variable. Thus there is no speculation, no mystery, no hypnotic suggestion and no sloth. A new science of man beckons us to throw off the shackles of tradition.

At school levels or later, education in tension control can conserve energy and promote efficient living. It is open to all mankind.

Evidence and methods will be discussed in the following pages. These will be presented in such a manner as to give this book maximal usefulness in regard to the practice of medicine in any of its branches. To enhance further this usefulness, the material in Chapter 6 is made available as a separate pamphlet, with a text specially written to serve as a guide for home practice by the patient. A copy of the pamphlet (*Self-Operations Control*) will be found at the back of the book. Additional copies may be ordered from J. B. Lippincott Co., Philadelphia 5, Pa.

EDMUND JACOBSON

Acknowledgments

Richard Lange and Bernardine Lufkin have contributed much in spirit to the present manuscript. In addition, Dick has carried out the measurements and made the graphs and diagrams, often adding his own ingenuity. Bernardine has done much on the references, and her judgment on expression of principles has been consulted frequently. My wife, Beth, has always been available, ready to say "yes" or "no" when called upon for her opinion.

Never to be forgotten are the contributions of the Bell Telephone Laboratories to my earlier endeavors. In the beginning, without prospect of personal gain, H. A. Frederick and D. G. Blattner, electronic engineers, wholeheartedly devoted their genius to my aims and orientation. Over them, was A. B. Arnold and, later, Oliver E. Buckly—chairmen of research, until the latter became President of these Laboratories. Their interest and proferred help was unflagging. Last, but not least, I mention my great friend, Mervin Kelley. When he succeeded to the title of President, he became servitor to this nation on a scale which the public has never realized. I owe him much and thank him as well as these other eminent men.

E. J.

Contents

Introduction

Efficiency: The Basic Aim of All Medical Practice

We doctors should become aware that efficiency is really the basic purpose of every scientific form of therapy. This applies equally to general practice and every specialty, including surgery. The surgeon operates to repair or substitute structure only because otherwise the individual might not be able to accomplish his daily duties as well. A painful organ, such as a gall-bladder, is removed or medicated really because, otherwise, the efficiency of the patient would be reduced, perhaps even to disability. What really matters is that the distress arouses wasteful energy expenditure in the form of neuromuscular tension, rendering accomplishment more costly. Analogously, we take our motor cars to shops for oiling, greasing and repairs only to maximize the achievement of these vehicles. This can be expressed readily in terms of efficiency, namely, the output in effective power per unit of input, which is chiefly gasoline.

Although our cars, like our bodies, often suffer from diminished efficiency, the only disadvantage in the car may be the cost of more gasoline per mile. When human beings suffer from diminished efficiency, the disadvantage is not merely the need for increased energy provision intake. Effort energy in human beings is expended chiefly in the form of muscle tension and relaxation, for about half the weight of the body generally is composed of muscle, and this tissue is the seat of every human effort. However, food taken by mouth is not ready for combustion for muscle tension; it must first be worked over in the body chemical laboratories to engender complicated phosphate substances such as adenosinetriphosphate. We cannot buy this substance ready-made, as we do gasoline for automobiles. Human energy wasted in excessive neuromuscular tension is not so easily replaced.

Consequences of Inefficiency

There is still another disadvantage in the human organism as compared with the automobile, in regard to inefficiency. When carburetors waste gas, there is little loss and, chiefly, the necessity of buying extra gasoline. But when wasteful tensions exist in the human organism, they interfere by physiologic inhibition with what the organism sets out to do as primary purpose. Also, fatigue and strain may result.

Mindful of these considerations, I have devoted much of my life to studies of human efficiency and how to maintain or increase it. Most effective, in my experience, have been methods of neuromuscular tension control, for they are direct.

By neuromuscular tension control, we seek to do by direct means what really is implied in every scientific form of therapy, namely, the restoration of efficiency. However, it has become clear that—whereas most forms of medicine or surgery seek, at most, restoration to normal—tension control methods, which are education, may cultivate a degree of efficiency even higher than is common in most healthy persons. In learning to play golf or any other form of athletics, one becomes more proficient; likewise, the aim of education in any field is increase in efficiency beyond that of the natural, untaught person. On the same principle, training in tension control can aim *farther* than mere relief of nervousness, anxiety or other emotion or functional syndromes. Beyond the attainment of relief there is the attainment of excellence.

Physicians who are familiar with progressive relaxation methods—the procedures for human efficiency which were investigated and developed in our laboratories and clinic—may well wonder how they are related to self-operations control, which is the subject of the present volume. Is this a new departure?

Scientific Foundations of Self-Operations Control

Self-Operations Control is a new, improved form of *pedagogy,* founded on the technics described as progressive or scientific relaxation, which have been proved clinically and in the laboratory. S.O.C. is new in that it inculcates habits of efficiency more readily when applied to suitable classes of people. It is indicated for people (including children) who have become adapted to the present push-button culture, so to speak, especially farmers, mechanics and most businessmen. Such persons are capable of running instruments such as motor cars, and they take naturally to switches and other control devices. Self-Operations Control is engineering applied to medicine and, thus, may be looked on as a combined discipline. Equally well, it may be called "self-engineering" or "neuromuscular self-control." The doctor may select whatever term he prefers.

Before the development of the new pedagogy, progressive relaxation had been employed for all classes of people. Today, I prefer this generic method for philosophers and abstract thinkers, including many lawyers, and for women who think mostly of dress or bridge. Progressive relaxation thus may apply better to certain classes of people, however brilliant, but it also applies generally to backward people, including those types and races who have never had experience in running instruments.

Control Tests

As scientists who wish to determine the therapeutic results of Self-Operations Control, we shall need to apply it alone when possible, omitting any other therapeutic measures, such as sedatives, tranquilizers or other drugs, vacations, hobbies or psychotherapy. We must carry the principle of introducing only one variable for test even to the point of insisting that the patient continue otherwise unchanged in his living habits of hours of rest and work, occupation, diet, smoking and drinking, etc.

In addition, there will be cases of another class from which we can learn much; namely, cases in which other measures are, indeed, being used and are duly recorded. However, in these combined therapies, any favorable or unfavorable results obviously should be ascribed not to Self-Operations Control alone but to the combination.

On the laboratory side, the problems for investigation are the same for both methods, as was implied in stating that the difference is chiefly pedagogic. Accordingly, the reader will find evidence supporting the use of Self-Operations Control methods in the Bibliography at the end of this volume, including *Progressive Relaxation,* first published by the University of Chicago Press in 1929.

As will appear in the following pages, Self-Operations Control is cultivated self-engineering. The patient learns to operate himself somewhat as he learns to run a motor car. Just as the car has wheels by which it performs in terms of power output, so he has muscles by which he performs in terms of power output. Every performance of the car can be stated substantially in terms of what its wheels do on the ground. Likewise, every effort-performance of the patient can be stated in terms of what his muscles do in three-dimensional space.

It takes time for any beginner to grasp that, in the human being, the visual, auditory and other image and tension patterns which he learns to observe are, to him, symbols, carrying meanings which may represent the nth degree of abstraction. Thus he recalls, imagines and fancies what is real or what is not.

It takes time also for him fully to realize that the muscle sense is a built-in device of nature which he can employ usefully to estimate his every effort-energy cost, however grossly and vaguely. Step by step, with daily observation and practice, this becomes as familiar as does driving a car. Also, it becomes of daily use.

When anyone drives a car, he employs the controls on the dashboard. Analogously, when anyone learns to run himself, he can do so by means of the control devices in the muscle spindles.

So much for a brief picture in advance. We turn now to our medical needs.

CHAPTER 1

The Medical Need
for Self-Operations
Control

Forty years of medical practice have convinced me that we may look forward to a drastic change in coming decades. In general, most patients doubtless receive prescriptions, surgery or advice to their satisfaction, but it appears that, as a rule, their emotional needs—which play an important role in bringing them to the doctor's office—are neither adequately understood nor adequately met.

Importance of Emotional Reaction

Very gradually, physicians are coming to realize that emotional reactions are of primary significance not only in functional but also in organic disorders such as essential hypertension, coronary heart disease, peptic ulcer and hyperthyroidism. However, medical philosophy is still considerably tainted with the obsolescent view that mind and body are two more or less discrete realms. Indeed, this still colors the thinking even of many nonpracticing scientists, although evidence has been accumulating that all mental activities are as much a function of the combined action of the nervous and the muscular systems as are digestion and locomotion.* Anatomi-

* For references, see Bibliography, pp. 207 to 210.

1

cally, the nervous and the muscle systems can be dissected apart, but, in the functioning organism, they act as a unified circuitous network. Evidently, medical understanding and practice will need to evolve from the dogmas dominant 60 years ago toward a more integrated approach.

This will come if and when we doctors realize that we can do much for our patients in addition to our prescriptions, our operations and our advice. It seems reasonable to expect that much of scientific medical practice of the future may well lie in teaching the patient to do for himself better than drugs can do for him, in certain respects. Accordingly, in order to secure better results with many of his patients in daily practice, the doctor might profitably look into physiology for scientific understanding of the emotions of his patient with intent to teach some effective measure of control. He will find that control measures bring therapeutic results that are not common after standard measures of therapy, whether drugs, diet, surgery or psychotherapy.

The Doctor Becomes Instructor

This development will require the doctor to don the mantle of the educator. Skill in drug prescription is, without question, indispensible to every doctor, but now it has become possible to add to this skill the use of physiologic methods which can greatly enhance the benefits for which the patient comes to the doctor's office.

A speaker on essential hypertension at the 1962 meeting of the Interstate Postgraduate Medical Association of North America stated that, in his opinion, the most effective weapon against that disease lay in doctor-patient relations. Emphasis on the importance of this relationship is in good order—but you cannot teach a man to be a good pilot of a jet plane (for example) merely by establishing warm relations. Each patient, each person, lives a life dependent on his own self-management for the most part, but, unfortunately, how he performs this has been a matter of custom and habit, instead of science.

However, this naïve neglect surely is bound to give way if our culture progresses sufficiently. Certain scientists are beginning to realize the significance of "information processing" in the brain. They have begun to realize that, to this extent, man is an instrument, however great the complexity. In a symposium on this subject at the 1962 International Congress of Physiology in Leyden there were many brilliant discussions. However, it was generally not mentioned that man is not merely a computing instrument more complicated than all electronic models. These scientists were so preoccupied with the "decisions" in the nervous system that they neglected wholly in their philosophy the role of *power* in human efforts.

Muscle Contraction is the Power Factor

Power resides primarily not in nervous impulses but in muscular contraction. It results from combustion, the breaking down of high phosphate bonds.* Networks of nerves, whether in the reticular substance or any other part, do not consist of closed circuits as electronic models do. The current conception that the brain can act in and by itself finds no support in the many electrophysiologic findings of 30 years in my laboratory or in others. My findings make it safe to assume that by and large there are *no closed circuits in the brain.*† Instead, the brain circuits are completed not alone in neurones but, commonly, also in muscle fibers. In other words, my findings, confirmed by others, make the concept that the brain thinks and then the muscle acts outdated. Nevertheless, this childish cliché is common currency and, unknown to us, influences our daily medical practice to no good end.

Based on a working conception of the power (as well as the information) factor in our every effort, we doctors can now apply this new knowledge practically. In the following pages

---

* Cf. Peterson, R. D., *et al.* in the Bibliography.

† The term "circuit" is, of course, used here in a different sense from an electrical circuit consisting of a battery and wires. Nerve impulses are the passage of polarization changes in the surface of fibers.

reasons will be given for assuming that we can teach our patients self-engineering to their great advantage and to ours.

Patient Benefits

What are the possible gains to the patient if he learns habitually to observe his tension-image patterns quickly and correctly and learns self-operations control? From long clinical experience as well as reports of many patients, a partial list can be offered as follows:

1. The patients gain a better understanding of themselves and others, and this is found to be satisfying and enjoyable as well as practical.

2. They learn to recognize and locate undue tensions and to relax them toward moderation during moments of stress. Most patient value this gain.

3. By this physiologic psychotherapy the patient becomes independent. He does not rely on therapeutic suggestions or autosuggestions, which cultivate dependence; these have no place in present methods—and are, indeed, to be avoided. (Similarly, teachers of other skills do not train by methods based on suggestion. For example, pilots are not trained to talk to themselves about favorable results, but are trained to observe and act accordingly.)

4. Patients tend to become less worrisome, less hypochondriac, less dependent on others.

5. Progressively diminished tension tends to become a matter of habit by day as well as by night, replacing former hyperirritability and emotional overexcitement.

6. Patients learn to adapt better to the conditions of life.

7. Especially, they learn to meet difficulties and misfortunes and, thus, become better prepared for living.

8. As a rule, they sleep better and avert fatigue better.

9. If they are able to work, they can do so effectively with less tension, thus saving pathologic wear and tear on vital organs. When it is necessary, they can work longer hours.

10. Patients learn to distinguish objective stimuli from subjective response to a degree not attained otherwise. In a word, they tend to become more objective.

11. Generally, attention and concentration tend to improve. (Excessive tension inhibits clear attention.)

12. The vegetative nervous system tends to become stabilized. (Complete control, of course, is neither possible nor desired.)

13. With advancing habits of relxation, clinical experience shows improvement in function of the digestive tract. Commonly, constipation or spells of diarrhea diminish (especially in the absence of severe infection).

14. It is probable that ulcer often can be averted. Methods of treating active ulcer should include self-operations control.

15. There is evidence that high nervous tension creates undue strain on heart and blood vessels. Dr. Christiernin, former chief physician of the Metropolitan Life Insurance Company, was convinced that the key to reducing the high death rate from cardiovascular disease is application of progressive relaxation.

16. Essential hypertension generally responds by a reduction of diastolic as well as systolic pressure. In early conditions, our studies suggest that there may be lasting reduction to normal in many instances.

17. In functional nervous conditions, neuroses and psychoneuroses, tension control methods seem to be specific. Often, after other methods have failed, improvement comes with dramatic promptness.

18. Lowering of tension by my clinical methods is commonly advocated by many specialists in other fields, including dermatology, urology, ophthalmology and general surgery, who have seen encouraging results.

19. Emotional patients in every doctor's practice doubtless have much to gain if they learn self-operations control.

20. In general, it may be assumed that, in anyone, healthy or not, economy of energy thus attained adds effectively to welfare response.

Advantages to the Doctor

It is of economic advantage to the physician that he give his attention to as many patients as possible, provided that his work is thorough. Control methods permit this admirably, for, if the physician has several rooms, he can attend to a patient in each since each patient is also his own teacher and profits the more during an hour of instruction if the doctor comes and goes. During World War Two, class instruction of naval air cadets in progressive relaxation included as many as 500 in one period, attended by five naval instructors.

Among other advantages, the doctor, in teaching self-operations control, will protect his own health. A good instructor in this field must practice what he preaches in order to give the patient an example to follow. The patient is impressed when he sees how much can be accomplished by the busy doctor who is relaxed even when he is working. In turn, the doctor can save himself, to some extent, from fatigue and the more serious consequences of overwork. The fear of eventual coronary disease or a stroke can be met by taking better care of his own tensions. A Medical News report to doctors appeared in the Journal of the American Medical Association of September 22, 1962 under the heading, "You May Be Sicker than You

Think." It stated that preliminary analysis of the pathology tests run at the A.M.A. exhibit laboratory in Chicago in June indicated that two thirds of the physicians tested had significant abnormalities.

We all believe in the periodic examination, yet, very frequently, we do nothing about it. However, there is a real need for the doctor to do something for himself as well as for his patient. For this as well as for the public advantage it is hoped that doctors generally will take up self-operations control.

CHAPTER 2

Everybody Is
Subject to Anxiety

"This is the age of anxiety." These words from the daily column of a well known physician reflect the recognition that anxiety today is wide-spread.[*]

To the neuropsychiatrist, anxiety states are familiar. He notes them in various phases, mild or severe, transient or lasting, in most of his patients, possibly in every one. From one view or another they are the general concern of humanity. Dramatists and writers of serious fiction pose their problems and present their solutions. The classic tragedies of the Hebrews and the Greeks owe much of their hold on mankind to their recital of anxious reaction. In modern fiction the recital is continued. I am informed that the phrase "age of anxiety" appeared first in a poem by W. H. Auden and that this poem was set to music about a decade ago by Leonard Bernstein and that this has been expressed in ballet.

The universal occurrence of anxiety is illustrated in Hamlet's soliloquy, often classed as the greatest speech in all literature:

> To be or not to be—that is the question:
> Whether 'tis nobler in the mind to suffer
> The slings and arrows of outrageous fortune
> Or to take arms against a sea of troubles,

---

[*] Van Dellen, T. R.: Tranquility at a Price, Chicago Daily Tribune, Nov. 18, 1959.

And by opposing end them. To die—to sleep—
No more: and by a sleep to say we end
The heart-ache and the thousand natural shocks
That flesh is heir to. 'Tis a consummation
Devoutly to be wished. To die—to sleep.
To sleep—perchance to dream: ay, there's the rub!
For in that sleep of death what dreams may come
When we have shuffled off this mortal coil,
Must give us pause. There's the respect
That makes calamity of so long life.
For who would bear the whips and scorns of time,
The oppressor's wrong, the proud man's contumely,
The pangs of despised love, the law's delay,
The insolence of office and the spurns
That patient merit of the unworthy takes,
When he himself might his quietus make
With a bare bodkin? Who would these fardels bear,
To grunt and sweat under a weary life,
But that the dread of something after death—
The undiscovered country, from whose bourn
No traveler returns—puzzles the will,
And makes us rather bear those ills we have
Than fly to others that we know not of?
Thus conscience doth make cowards of us all,
And thus the native hue of resolution
Is sicklied o'er with the pale cast of thought,
And enterprises of great pith and moment
With this regard their currents turn awry
And lose the name of action.

Shakespeare's mouthpiece for mankind questions the worth
of life itself which abounds with difficulties that we must face,
or become broken in the encounter. Aside from the poetic
wording, Hamlet's complaints are much like those of our
patients.

The reader will be able to continue the account begun above,
illustrating it with the manifold trials and anxieties taken from
his own life.

Resort to Religion and/or Philosophy

Most often the person afflicted with anxious states resorts to
religious faith or to some form of philosophizing. He compares
and he generalizes until he composes himself more or less by
conceiving his problem in a larger setting. Often he calls on

the common experience of mankind as expressed in some saying or adage, "It might have been worse!" or "Behind each
cloud is a silver lining!" Other current phrases in America
include: "Good will triumph!" "Rome wasn't built in a day!"
"Chin up!" "Take it easy! Relax!" "Laugh and the world
laughs with you!" "Weep and you weep alone!" "Tomorrow
will be brighter!" "Things are not as bad as they seem!"
"Thy lot is the common lot of all!"

The literature of oriental peoples exhibits likewise a wide
range of exhortations against anxiety, overconcern and worry.

From times of yore, technical philosophers have sought to
devise ways to live which can free us from anxiety. Perhaps
the best known of philosophies of living is the Philosophy of
Stoicism, which was founded by Zeno (4th-3rd century B.C.).
Principally, the Stoics preached and practiced the curbing of
appetites and carnal desires. In consequence, the buffets of
fate would strike with diminished blows. There would be less
to lose.

Fear is the emotion that instigates this type of philosophy,
but its adherents evidently have not realized this and historians
have missed the point. Fear of losses has led these people to
dispossess themselves of various riches of life. It is a negative
way of life.

Zeno, the leader in this philosophy, lived to a ripe old age.
According to the accounts, he injured one thumb or broke one
finger. Presumably he applied his philosophy or attempted to
do so. However, the digit continued to prove troublesome,
leading him to solve his problem by suicide.* This sad end
perhaps attests for all time the bankruptcy of philosophy as a
sufficient means of handling anxious states.

Relief through Drink and Drugs

For transient relief of mild gloom man often resorts to
beverages, especially those based on caffeine or on alcohol.
For centuries, indeed, the fermented grape and other fruit or

---

* Diogenes Laertius: Lives of Eminent Philosophers, Hicks, R. D., trans.,
Cambridge, Mass., Harvard University Press, 1950.

vegetable product, tobacco and coca leaves and the seed of the opium poppy have been the basis of substances which lighten anxiety tension. In addition, modern man has been furnished with a formidable armamentorium against anxious states. Many of the newer drugs have been proved to be useful for temporary relief, as in patients awaiting operation. Also they may prove to be useful as a second best to physicians who will not take the time to learn physiologic measures of anxiety control or to apply them in practice. However, there can be too much of a good thing. Under the direction of pharmaceutical organizations and the physicians reached by their teachings, high pressure business is having an impressive influence on the habits of mankind. Stockholders, at least, derive great benefit. In the United States alone during the year 1958, according to published estimates, 757,000 pounds of barbiturates were produced. Since each pound accounts for about 4,600 doses, the figures indicate that about 10,000,000 doses were employed on the order of three per day by about 13,000,000 people.

Miltown was produced in the amount of 759,000 pounds. There are about 1,000 doses per pound. The figures indicate the usage, if estimated at three per day, by about 1,000,000 people. Other tranquilizers were produced in the amount of 205,000 pounds, amounting to about 18,000,000 doses of 50 mg.* From the figures quoted, it is evident that many of our people are living a drugged life.

Opposition to the use of drugs against anxiety in meeting the problems of life has appeared among physicians and has been voiced in medical journals† and in the public press. Van Dellen writes:

There are millions who rely on tranquilizers instead of self-control. They want peace of mind without the discipline. . . . Our modern tranquilizers do not cure; they hold the conflict in abeyance until the individual is able to fend for himself.‡

Unfortunately, the attainment of this end is commonly

---

* Drugs and Cosmetics, Jan. or Feb., 1959.
† Editorial, Scientific Relaxation. New Eng. J. Med. 256:713-714, 1957.
‡ Van Dellen, T. R.: Tranquillity at a Price, Chicago Daily Tribune, Nov. 18, 1959.

impeded or prevented by the habitual use of tranquilizers. The crutch becomes the daily mode of living. It is safe to say that no person is fully himself when under the influence of sedatives or tranquilizers. Thus the extensive use of drugs against anxiety is contrary to sound thinking. Modern man plunges into drugs seeking escape from trial and difficulty.

If anxiety is the foremost of the emotions depicted in most classic drama, mankind should not neglect the lesson which is taught: "Though suffering often cannot be avoided, it can be nobly endured.* "Sweet are the uses of adversity!"† An outstanding illustration is the Book of Job.‡

As certain psychiatrists have pointed out recently, life stripped of anxiety would become devoid of challenge.§ Highlights diminish or disappear, leaving only a dull gray. The many who live on sedatives pay inordinately for relief. Nevertheless, the popularity and the extensive use of these drugs points to the need for better means to prevent and control excessive anxiety.

Failure of These Measures

Satisfactory anxiety control has not resulted from the many efforts of philosophers and would-be philosophers, or from the products of the pharmaceutical houses. The many sufferers from this condition coming to the Jacobson Clinic characteristically give a history of chronic addiction to sedatives and tranquilizers, often with sad side-effects. In daily practice the average neuropsychiatrist today is obliged to cope with the anxieties of almost every patient as best he can. For want of something better, he commonly resorts to general advice to his patient aided by sedatives and tranquilizers of various types. Sometimes these include even antihistamines. According to the school of thought which he prefers, he may follow the teach-

---

* Faverty, E.: Your Literary Heritage, p. 27, Lippincott, Phila., 1959.
† Shakespeare, W.: As You Like It. Act I, Sc. 3, line 123.
‡ Kallen, H. M.: The Book of Job as a Greek Tragedy. New York, N. Y., Hill and Wang, 1959.
§ Dickel, H. A., and Dixon, H. H.: Inherent dangers in use of tranquilizing drugs in anxiety states, J. A. M. A. *163*:422-426, 1957.

ings of Freud, Jung, Adler or those of some more recent writer. Many a psychoanalyst adds his own individual touch.

Need for Scientific Understanding

Since anxiety is spread over human experience in every era, we shall go far if and when we achieve a science of this emotion. To understand anxiety will be to know what man does when he perceives, evaluates and reacts to danger, real or imaginary. We shall test our new-found knowledge crucially when we set out to control anxiety; this will be the proof of the pudding. This knowledge, if it really becomes ours, will apply to man's every response, not only to danger. Furthermore, it will reveal precisely how he represents reality to himself and how he merely imagines. Although bold, let this be our undertaking—to build foundations wide and deep, sufficient to support a giant-structure—if only an increasing number of scientists can be attracted to build a science of man himself!

In the present volume, the attempt is made to show that anxiety states can be subjected to strict scientific study, exactly as can conditions of the heart, and that scientific measures have now become available for direct control of anxiety states. The measures to be employed are highly technical, and, in view of the many attempts to "cure" anxiety which have been advocated up to date, some doctors may have become convinced by their experience that control is impossible. However, 50 years ago many people doubted that it would ever be possible to produce and fly a "heavier than air" machine. This feat would never have been accomplished had mankind resorted to doubts or to speculative approaches alone. The flight of Daedelus toward the sun by means of eagle's feathers did not introduce actual flight for man. Flight required not only imagination but also certain technical procedures of engineering science based upon theoretic physics. Today, likewise, it is reasonable to expect that an effective answer to anxiety will result only when appropriate technical science has been developed and applied.

We should not be surprised if thus we are led into branches of basic science as yet little employed by most practicing doctors, for there is nothing more complex than the human mind with which we doctors have to deal. Accordingly, we may be required to forge our tools from more than one of the basic sciences. Also, we may be obliged to relinquish some of the engaging ideologies which have lured many to date.

If we are to perform a basic task vital for mankind, we may begin with a comparison of the educational means proposed here with the medicinal measures which predominate in the clinical practice of most doctors today. This will be discussed in the following chapter.

CHAPTER 3

Shall We Teach or
Medicate?

Requirements for Sound Evidence: Controlled Conditions

Whatever methods we employ with our patients, our preferences certainly should be based on sound evidence. However, the human organism is the most extremely complex variable with which science has to deal. Added to this complexity is the extremely intricate and continually changing character of anxiety and other neuropsychiatric states in every patient. Therefore, sound evidence in regard to any method of therapy in this field is difficult to obtain. Physicians know that, in maladies of every variety except malignancy, Nature improves or cures frequently. Thus, improvement following an alleged remedy may not be real proof of efficacy. As A. J. Carlson emphasized, we should avoid the fallacy, *post hoc, ergo propter hoc.*

In general, the effects of any measure can be estimated best if it is employed without additional measures of therapy.

However, it is no easy matter to exclude from the life of any patient other variables that may aid his condition. This requires him to continue in his usual occupation, working or playing hours, hours in bed, diet and so on, along with other measures of experimental control. Furthermore, he must not change his habits of exercise, use of alcoholic and other bever-

14

ages, smoking and personal associations. Finally, if a medicinal or a nonsuggestive form of psychotherapy is to be tested, we must avoid influencing him suggestively in its favor.

Change One Variable Only

The requirements for reliable conclusions on the efficacy of a particular form of therapy are indeed difficult to secure in any department of medicine, but most difficult of all in connection with anxiety states and other chronic emotional disorders. Strictly speaking, if a medication is to be tested, it should be done without the aid of psychotherapy; otherwise, it is impossible to determine whether a favorable or unfavorable result is due, in whole or in part, to the psychotherapy or the medication. Of course, the same precaution applies to any endeavor to test any method of psychotherapy: simultaneous medication and other measures which might favor recovery must be carefully avoided.

To what extent are these obviously necessary measures currently employed in research in either psychotherapy or medicinal therapy? The author's answer is, "Infrequently! Most claims in either field are based on data from investigations that are not sufficiently controlled!"

In the present investigations on the results of teaching the anxious patient how to adapt himself, I have been most aware of the requirements mentioned above and have made a practice of explaining them carefully to my patients at the outset of instruction. They have been informed why they will be required to maintain the *status quo* as much as possible. For example, if they smoke excessively, they are to continue to do so; otherwise, how could we know to what degree, if any, a change in their emotional state (for better or worse) should be attributed to the moderation in smoking rather than our method? Further, I have explained to them that they will receive instruction at their own risk and on their own responsibility, without promises or guarantees—just as if they were entering a course of mathematics or engineering.

Saving of Time vs. Achievement of Independence

As compared with educational methods applied to anxiety neurosis, medicinal treatment offers time-saving advantages to the over-busy physician and, often, to his patient. He can select a tranquilizer or sedative very rapidly and write a prescription. Even the captious patient commonly can be impressed sufficiently to give it a trial. Indeed, the doubting Thomas generally is less prone to sit in the judgment seat when medicines are prescribed—excepting, of course, those of our population who are inclined to Christian science or some other form of drugless healing. However, we doctors should realize that many others of our population harbor strong disapproval of the use of sedatives and tranquilizers. In this chapter we shall examine to what extent, if any, this disapproval is warranted and even protective.

The aims of the present methods are to teach, inculcate and favor initiative and drive of the patient to meet duties, difficulties and pleasures with adaptive success. These methods stress the development of greater independence as a rule, and, particularly, in those neurotic types that are inclined to depend on the physician. *Tension Control methods seek for the patient greater freedom from anxieties, phobias, disabling fears and other forms of excessive emotions.* In a word, they stress freedom from disabling inhibitions.

Undesirability of Complete Elimination of Fear

Without doubt, however, freedom from inhibitions can be carried too far. Morality, manners and law itself are founded largely on specific inhibitions. Complete freedom from anxiety and fear might prove as undesirable as complete freedom from pain sensation. The occasional infant born without the protection of the pain sensory function soon becomes crippled. In battle, complete fearlessness can lead to speedy catastrophe. Fearlessness in pedestrians crossing the road and in automobile drivers are other examples with frequent catastrophic consequences. Therefore, the present aim is the elimination of anxiety or fearfulness—not completely, but only to the extent that it is pathologic, harmful, overprotective or wasteful of energy. Our aim can be toward the golden mean—to control anxiety and fear in favor of more efficient and successful living. We shall not teach our patients to loaf their lives away or to behave as if they are under a heavy dose of sedative or tranquilizer. We do not teach them to live as vegetables. Our aim always will be effectiveness in action as well as effectiveness in securing rest and recuperation. In other words, adaptive success in the life of our patients, freely secured by their own initiative, precludes *excessive* relaxation when meeting their problems and difficulties. I propose to make them better able to do this for themselves. This has become possible because scientific advance in neurophysiology now gives us a secure base for advance in neuropsychiatric methods.

Except in rare instances, I do not propose that the doctor try to solve the patient's problems for him by advising him how to change his environment, his position, his mate or other personal relation or circumstance. Generally, we have found that tension control technics enable the patient to solve his difficulties and to find his way better than he did previously— often, better than we could devise. (This will be illustrated in a later chapter.) Thus, both theory and practical results point to the need for and the advantage of achieving through technical instruction a freedom and an independence which no drug can give.

For this achievement (as for psychotherapy in general), as compared with dispensing sedatives and tranquilizers, we doctors shall have to pay the price of additional time and effort devoted to our patients; and they, in turn, will have to pay, in the form of their own time devoted to daily practice for learning purposes.

Concomitant Use of Drugs and Sedatives

Tension control methods are by no means to be identified with "drugless healing." Most of the patients who are referred to my clinic are more or less habituated to the use of sedatives and/or tranquilizing drugs before they come. In practice, the patient often is told to continue with the medicines which he has been taking but to discontinue them gradually if and when he becomes ready and able to do so as instruction proceeds. Occasionally, I prescribe a change in the medication if either loss of effect from prolonged use or unfavorable side-effects have occurred.

I sometimes favor the use of sedatives or tranquilizing medication as a crutch until the patient learns to stand on his own feet—but only if the patient comes to me so habituated. If he has not been using depressants, I do not prescribe them as a rule. However, under special conditions, e.g., when something prevents the attendance of the patient for instruction or prevents the doctor from seeing him when necessary, it may seem advisable to prescribe some medication. Also, when suicidal impulses seem to be uncontrolled, I may prescribe depressants or even electroshock therapy.*

While sedation and tranquilization by drugs thus have a recognized place in medical practice, there can be too much of a good thing! The widespread use of drugs for calming purposes is regarded by many physicians as a menace of our times. I believe it wise to emphasize and reiterate that *no person can be wholly master of his own powers when he is under the influence of a sedative or tranquilizing drug.* This has been recognized by the Pennsylvania Medical Society commission, which studied fatal accidents on the Pennsylvania Turnpike over a 10-year period. The commission suggested (1961) that doctors advise patients of the dangers inherent in the use of tranquilizers, amphetamine, antihistamines and other drugs that may lessen a driver's ability to control his automobile.

Before employing pharmacologic remedies in anxiety states, physicians should think carefully. They should distinguish cases in which anxiety supervenes when a person who is nervous and emotional, but otherwise normal, meets difficulties which overpower him from those cases in which the patient is

---

* In over 40 years of practice this has seemed indicated only in three cases.

diseased, as in cyclothymia, involutional melancholia or schizophrenia, and, as the direct result of this illness, develops undue anxiety. Here the imbalance possibly may be chemical in etiology, and, eventually, we may hope to see effective means of chemical treatment. However, in the anxious world of today it can be misleading to look to chemical treatment to solve the patient's problems for him.

Advances in Psychopharmacology

With these reservations, it still may be assumed that research in scientific departments of psychopharmacology and pharmacologic institutions is making striking advances. I hope that such advances will continue for centuries to come. It is my conviction that every practicing physician ought to keep up with current literature in this field. The following outline of the treatment of anxiety by medicinal means is admittedly only a brief sketch but may serve as a framework. A complete review is beyond the scope or the intention of the present volume.*

BARBITURATES

The action of barbiturates in depressing the central nervous system and/or other systems is not yet fully known. Among various hypotheses are the following: these substances may inhibit brain respiration by blocking a step in the electron transport system,† they may block the dehydrogenase enzyme system at the entrance of pyruvic acid into the Krebs cycle;‡ they may produce synaptic block;§ in the case of pentobarbital in small doses, it may exert an anti-inhibitory action on certain dendritic synapses;‖ they may reduce concomitantly cerebral

---

* The reader may refer to LaVerne, A. A.: Compendium of neuropsychopharmacology, J. Neuropsych. 2:212-220, 1961.

† Greig, M. E.: The site of action of narcotics on brain metabolism, J. Pharmacol. Exp. Ther. 87:185, 1946.

‡ Persky, H., Goldstein, M. S., and Levine, R.: The enzymatic mechanism of barbiturate action, J. Pharmacol. Exp. Ther. 100:273, 1950.

§ Bishop, P. D., McLeod, J. G.: Nature of potentials associated with synaptic transmission in lateral geniculate of cat, J. Neurophysiol. 17:387, 1954.

‖ Purpura, D. P.: In Psychopharmacology, pp. 196-197, (H. H. Pennes, Ed.), New York, Hoeber-Harper, 1958.

metabolic rate and mental function when they produce intoxication;* like narcotics, they may inhibit high-energy phosphate
formation directly or by depressing the high-energy phosphate
formation necessary for the acetylation process, thus resulting
in levels of acetylcholine so diminished as to be insufficient to
maintain neural activities required for the waking state;† they
may lengthen recovery time from refractory period;‡ they
may act selectively on internuncial neurones in the cortex
rather than on the afferent pathway.§ For the present we
must admit that how barbiturates and other anesthetizing substances suppress synaptic transmission has not been established.

According to recent theories, barbiturates and other anesthetics in high concentrations block nerve impulse conduction
as well as synaptic transmission. With lower doses, synaptic
transmission alone is affected. The reticular-activating system
of Morruzi and Magoun presumably is altered by barbiturate
activity. This system possibly maintains the conscious state by
transmittal of impulses to the cortex, whereupon there is wake-
fulness and the EEG shows desynchronization.‖

Himwich attributes the action of barbiturates (narcotics) to
"two potent influences." "The first is metabolic, a withdrawal

---

* Fazekas, J. F., and Bessman, A. N.: Coma mechanisms, Am. J. Med. *15:*
804, 1953.
† Govier, W. M., and Gibbons, A. J.: Pentobarbital inhibition of sulfanilamide
acetylation in pigeon liver extracts, Science *119:*185, 1954. McLennan, H., and
Elliot, K. A. C.: Effects of convulsant and therapeutic drugs on acetylcholine
synthesis, J. Pharmacol. Exp. Ther. *103:*35, 1951. Johnson, W. J., and Quastel,
J. H.: Narcotics and biological acetylations, Nature (London) *171:*602, 1953.
‡ Marshall, W. H.: Observations on subcortical somatic sensory mechanisms
of cat and monkey, J. Neurophysiol. *4:*25-43, 1941. Marshall, W., Woolsey,
C. N., and Bard, P.: Observations on cortical somatic sensory mechanisms of
cats under nembutal anesthesia, J. Neurophysiol. *4:*1-24, 1941.
§ Cf. Chang, Hsiang-Tung: The Evoked Potentials, *in* Field, John (ed.):
Handbook of Neurophysiology, Chap. 12, Sec. 1, Vol. 1, p. 308, Am. Physiol.
Soc., Washington.
‖ Moruzzi, G., and Magoun, H. W.: Brain stem reticular formation and the
activation of the EEG, Electroenceph. Clin. Neurophysiol. *1:*455, 1949. French,
J. D., and King, E. E.: Mechanisms involved in the anesthetic state, Surgery
*38:*228 1955. French, J. D., Verzeano, M., and Magoun, H. W.: An extra-
lemniscal sensory system in the brain, Arch. Neurol. Psychiat. *69:*505, 1953.
French, J. D., Verzeano, M., and Magoun, H. W.: A neural basis for the
anesthetic state, Arch. Neurol. Psychiat. *69:*519, 1953.

of energy required for support of the brain; the second is a direct interference with nervous activity . . . elevation of the synaptic threshold . . . not necessarily equally throughout the nervous system."*

Barbiturates are among the depressants most widely prescribed today. They include phenobarbital (5-ethyl-5-phenylbarbituric acid), sodium pentobarbital (for prolonged hypnotic or sedative action) sodium secobarbital (for more rapid onset but less persistent effect) and, also, sodium amobarbital, the relaxant effect of which on neuromuscular activity of man has been recorded in our laboratory.† A wide variety of other barbiturates are also in vogue.

Among the disadvantages in the clinical use of these popular drugs is a tendency to develop dependency and habituation in the patient. As a rule, side-effects vary from individual to individual. In some, the "hang-over" appears as a state of disturbed emotion or emotional imbalance.

The doctor recognizes barbiturate anesthesia and chronic addiction as *intoxication,* but he is perhaps not fully aware that the common English word for toxin is poison. However, we doctors should admit that *no person under the influence of a barbiturate can be fully himself.*

BROMIDES

When the quieting influence of bromides first came into prominence, we are reminded by P. Bailey, it was hailed as marking a new era in medicine. A similar enthusiasm, he finds, is currently in evidence in regard to the accomplishments of tranquilizing drugs.‡ My own study suggested that, in the amounts customary in therapeutic dosage, bromides have very little relaxant effect on neuromuscular responses.§

---

* Himwich, H. E.: Brain Metabolism and Cerebral Disorders, pp. 326-359, Williams and Wilkins, Baltimore, 1951.

† The last three barbiturates are familiar to doctors under trade names, respectively, Nembutal, Seconal and Sodium Amytal.

‡ Bailey, P.: The Academic Lecture, Am. J. Psychiat. *113:*387-406, 1956.

§ Jacobson, E.: Direct measurements of the effects of bromides, Sodium Amytal and of caffeine in man, Ann. Int. Med. *21:*455-468, 1944.

TRANQUILIZING DRUGS

The probable action of tranquilizing drugs is commonly believed to be specific inhibition of one or another enzyme system. This has been termed biochemical antagonism. Strecker cites four groups:

(1) Substances which compete with the substrate for the active sites in the enzyme; these include malonic acid* and the inhibitors of amine oxidase activity such as ephedrine. (2) Substances which compete with the coenzyme for an essential enzymic site, for example, the antivitamins. (3) Substances which react with the catalytic centers of the enzyme protein; these contain the organic phosphate cholinesterase inhibitors and the many SH poisons. (4) Substances such as fluoride or thiaminase, which inhibit enzymatic activity by reacting with coenzymes.†

To these Strecker adds a fifth group provisionally: substances which may prove to be biochemical antagonists of enzymes not yet determined.†

Strecker found evidence that chlorpromazine (Thorazine hydrochloride); 2-chloro-10-(3-dimethylaminopropyl) phenothiazine) inhibits the transfer of electrons from DPNH to oxygen at a number of sites by particles derived from brain mitochondria.‡ The use of chlorpromazine in anxiety states is familiar to doctors. Many patients, however, complain severely of side-effects. This drug progressively inhibits respiration in brain slices in vitro.§

Phenothiazines also are frequently prescribed for tranquilization. Their action possibly has to do with serotonin and norepinephrine, which (unlike ephedrine) are normally present in the brain and are found in greatest concentration in primitive areas, such as the midbrain and the hypothalamus. Accordingly, it is commonly believed that serotonine and norepinephrine have to do with emotion. Like reserpine, serotonin

---

* Quastel, J. H., and Wooldridge, W. R.: Some proteins of the dehydrogenating enzymes of bacteria, Biochem. J. 22:689, 1928.
† Strecker, H. J.: in Pennes, H. H. (ed.): Biochemistry of the Tranquilizing drugs in Psychopharmacology, p. 24, New York, Hoeber-Harper, 1958.
‡ Strecker, H. J.: ibid, p. 33.
§ Linden, O., Quastel, J. H., and Sved, S.: Effects of Chlorpromazine on Brain Metabolism in Vitro, in Pennes, H. H. (ed.): Psychopharmacology, pp. 1-22, New York, Hoeber-Harper, 1958.

contains an indole nucleus. The turnover of serotonin in the brain is rapid.* Norepinephrine is an oxidation product of epinephrine. The enzyme, monoamine oxidase, is believed to act on serotonin and norepinephrine, causing physiologic inactivation.† On this is based the clinical use of monoamine oxidase inhibitors, such as iproniazid and B-phenylisopropylhydrazine (Catron).

Cerebral synaptic transmission can be inhibited by serotonin, less so by norepinephrine and epinephrine.‡ Hess suggested that a subcortical system exists in which norepinephrine, like the sympathetic system, activates excitation (ergotropic action) but in which serotonin, like the parasympathetic system, produces apathy (trophotropic). According to this view, reserpine (an alkaloid) produces its effects by releasing serotonin and the phenothiazines by adrenergic blockade, blocking the action of norepinephrine.

It is important to emphasize that there are other views. Investigators are on the road to knowledge in this field but, as yet, have not arrived.

Both phenothiazines and barbiturates depress the reticular activating system, thus eliminating it as a source of emotional behavior through the hypothalamus.§ Direct stimulation of the reticular system in animal preparations produces EEG changes similar to those recorded on arousal from sleep. The animal becomes alert. According to recent conceptions, the reticular activating system influences both sensory and motor output.‖ It has been called "the great integrating mechanism of the brain" which acts to unify response to complex environmental

---

* Udenfriend, S., Weissbach, H., and Bogdanski, D. F.: Biochemical findings relating to the action of serotonin, Ann. N. Y. Acad. Sci. 66:602, 1957.

† Brodie, B. B., Prockup, D. J., and Shore, P. A.: An interpretation of the action of psychotropic drugs, Postgrad. Med. 24:296, 1958.

‡ Marrazzi, A. S.: The effects of certain drugs on cerebral synapses, Ann. N. Y. Acad. Sci. 66:496, 507, 1957.

§ Himwich, H. E., Rinaldi, F., and Willis, D.: An examination of phenothiazine derivatives with comparisons of their effects on the alerting reaction, chemical structure and therapeutic efficiency, J. Nerv. Ment. Dis. 124:53, 57, 1956.

‖ Livingston, W. K., Haugan, F. P., and Brookhart, J. M.: Functional organization of the central nervous system, Neurology 4:485-496, 1954.

stimuli.* It is an internuncial pathway, extending through the bulb, the pontine and the mesencephalic areas as well as through the subthalamus, the hypothalamus and the ventromedial portion of the thalamus. It sends and receives fibers to and from various parts of the cerebral cortex, the cerebellum, the hypothalamus and internuncial pools at various levels. Thus, in its connections with the hypothalamus and other limbic areas, it presumably serves in the arousal of emotion. If so, depression of this system by phenothiazines might be expected to diminish the anxious state.†

However, it is not yet proved that in anxiety states phenothiazines really are the drugs of choice. The concentration of serotonin and norepinephrine in the brainstem has been shown to be doubled in the brainstem of rabbits, evoking symptoms of central stimulation on inhibition of monoamine oxidase (MAO inhibition).‡ Central excitation may be desirable in depression, but it would seem to be of dubious value in clinical anxiety states that are not marked by severe depression. In such clinical states the general usefulness of phenothiazines is not established.

Meprobamate (Miltown; 2-methyl-2-n-propyl-1,3 propanediol dicarbamate) is one of the most popular of tranquilizing agents in anxiety tension states. Dickel, Wood and Dixon found electromyographic evidence of muscle relaxing effect in tense, anxious and fatigued working people.§ Meprobamate is believed to act as a central voluntary muscle relaxant, but, it is claimed, does not produce impairment of physical or mental efficiency.

---

* French, J. D.: The reticular formation: the nature of the reticular activating system, J. Neurosurg. 15:97, 1958.

† For discussion, see Conference on Amine Oxidase Inhibitors, N. Y. Acad. Sci. Nov. 20-22, 1958: A Pharmacological Approach to the Study of the Mind, Springfield, Ill., Thomas, 1959.

‡ Biel, J. H., Drukker, A. E., Shore, P. A., Specter, S., and Brodie, B. B.: Effect of 1-phenyl-2 hydrazine; J. Am. Chem. Soc. 80:1519, 1958.

§ Dickel, H. A., Wood, J. A., and Dixon, H. H.: Electromyographic studies on meprobamate and the working anxious patient, Ann. N. Y. Acad. Sci. 67:780, 1957. See also Dixon, N. M.: Meprobamate, a clinical evaluation, Ann. N. Y. Acad. Sci. 67:772, 1957.

Recently introduced is a butanediol, (Ultran, 2-/p-chloro-phenyl-3-methyl-2, 3-butanediol) for calming overemotional states, including anxiety. It is said to be a mild relaxant, with no known undesirable side-effects. However, its use has been recommended for adjunctive rather than definitive therapy.

As remarked by Schneider and Sigg, it is surprising that a quieting effect characterizes substances as structurally different as reserpine, chlorpromazine and meprobamate.*

Summary

Great as has been the progress in laboratory and clinical knowledge of sedatives and tranquilizing drugs, there is as yet no established knowledge of precisely how they produce a calmative effect. In a particular case of anxiety reaction or psychoneurosis the clinician today is more likely to follow a predilection for a particular drug based on his past experience with other cases than to base his choice on established science. The difficulty of choice is increased by the differences in chemical structure of quieting drugs, the differences in the anxiety forms in individuals and in the symptom-complexes associated with anxiety and the striking individual differences in emotional reactions to the same drug. Also, liability to habituation, side-effects (including possible liver damage) and diminished efficiency must be taken into consideration.

Not the least among the disadvantages of drug-taking is dependence on their use, with resultant loss of self-confidence and emotional security.

Early reports on the use of tranquilizing drugs to calm agitated, aggressive or violent psychotic patients were so encouraging as to lead some physicians to predict that our large mental institutions would soon show a greatly diminished

---

* Reserpine is an indole alkaloid esterified with trimethoxybenzoic acid; chlorpromazine, as stated above, has phenothiazine structure, while meprobamate is unrelated in structure to either of these. Schneider, J. A., and Sigg, E. B.: Pharmacologic Analysis of Tranquilizing and Central Stimulating Effects, in Pennes, H. H. (ed.): Psychopharmacology, p. 76, New York, Hoeber-Harper, 1958.

population. However, in the last 6 years many patients who were discharged had to return; mental institutions are as full as ever. This has been considered to be evidence that drugs alone do not cure.

In contrast with the problems that attend the use of drugs, there is reason to believe patients who are taught to do without drugs will be better off in the long run. They will become independent and self-reliant. They may become able to avert relapse by their own know-how.

In the following chapters, evidence will be presented illustrating that the more we teach our anxious patients sound knowledge, personal self-control and the know-how to live in emotional security notwithstanding the many difficulties to which they need to adjust, the less we will need to rely on medication. The results can prove rewarding both to doctor and patient, compensating them for the time necessarily devoted to educational procedures.

CHAPTER 4

A New View of
Human Behavior
and Control*

Some of the responsibility for teaching people how to conserve their energies in the interests of health and personal
efficiency naturally falls on the doctor. The approach may be
in the form of common sense advice on rest and vacations,
without really showing the patient how to rest; or it may take
on a more scientific character in the form of technical instructions, either on how to relax physiologically, generally and
differentially, or how to run his organism in daily living. Procedures relating to the first have been described previously,†
and evidence of the interrelationship of neuromuscular and
mental activities has been fully discussed.‡ It has been shown
that, with progressive muscular relaxation, the knee-jerk and

---

* This chapter has been rewritten from Jacobson, E.: Neuromuscular controls
in man: methods of self-direction in health and in disease, Am. J. Psychol.
68:549-561, 1955; read in part before Section 1, Psychology, American Association for the Advancement of Science, Dec. 20, 1952.
† Jacobson, Edmund: Progressive relaxation, Ab. J. Psychol. 36:73-87, 1925;
Progressive Relaxation, pp. 164-189, 327-345, Univ. Chicago Press, rev. ed.,
1938.
‡ Jacobson, Edmund: Electrical measurements of neuromuscular states during mental activities, Am. J. Physiol. 91:567-608, 1930; 94:22-34, 1930; 95:
694-702, 1930; 95:703-712, 1930; 96:115-121, 1931; 96:122-125, 1931; 97:200-
209, 1931, Electrophysiology of mental activities, Am. J. Psychol. 44:677-694,
1932; Electrical measurements of mental activities in man, Trans. N. Y. Acad.
Sci. 2:272-273, 1946.

other reflexes dwindle or disappear,* along with mental activities, including emotions, with generalized neurogenic deactivation effects on the vegetative nervous system, in which the cardiovascular,† the gastrointestinal‡ and other systems participate.

Instruction on muscular energy conservation rests on evidence secured in studies on progressive relaxation. However, a new form of instruction has recently been developed. In the older methods of teaching physiologic relaxation, the individual is shown how to slow his energy expenditures in the interests of recuperation, when at rest, and of efficiency, when in action. However, the manner of presentation is chiefly, although not exclusively, on the negative side. However, in the newer instruction, the emphasis is strongly on the positive side also. The conception thus not only envelops that of relaxation methods, but constitutes a new approach with notable differences.

Two Teaching Methods

In the present volume we distinguish between two general types of methods of instruction, both of which derive from laboratory and clinical methodologies, carefully controlled by electrical measurements and other measures. The evidence for the validity of either method rests on approximately the same data, and the difference between the two methods is chiefly pedagogic. The two methodologies are *progressive relaxation* —the original method, including various abridged forms of relaxation therapy—and *self-operations control,* in which the individual learns to run his organism according to what he

---

* Jacobson, Edmund, and Carlson, A. J.: The influence of relaxation upon the knee-jerk, Am. J. Physiol. 73:324-328, 1925.

† Jacobson, Edmund: Variation of blood pressure with skeletal muscle tension and relaxation, Ann. Int. Med. 12:1194-1212, 1939; The heart beat, Ann. Int. Med. 13:1619-1625, 1940; Variation in blood pressure with skeletal muscle tension, Am. J. Physiol. 126:546-547, 1939; Variation of blood pressure with brief voluntary muscular contractions, J. Lab. Clin. Med. 25:1029-1037, 1940; Cultivated relaxation in 'essential' hypertension, Arch. Phys. Ther. 21:645-654, 1940.

‡ Jacobson, Edmund: Spastic esophagus and mucous colitis, Arch. Int. Med. 39:453-445, 1927.

believes are its best interests. Thus he becomes his own
engineer, employing modern scientific know-how for personal
or other success.

Self-Operations Control

Previous studies of human activities from other laboratories
and clinics often have been devoted to the influences of
heredity plus those of habit formation; the "associationists" and
the Pavlovians have made innumerable fruitful contributions.
However, in the sciences of man, both theoretical and medical,
a distinguishing feature can be discerned from a new angle.
This feature is the possibility of man acquiring more autogenous control—greater ability to run his organism in its best
interests. Just as, when a valley has been accurately surveyed
from the top of a hillock, another site may be selected, afford-
ing a different view, so now we set our instruments up on a
new point of vantage and look on the activities of man not
solely from the conventional points of instinct and impulse,
or reflex function and habit formation but from that of his
opportunity to run his organism efficiently notwithstanding the
pressures and the stresses of his environment. Clinical evidence
has disclosed that the employment of this very opportunity can
be made habitual to a marked degree, with a view not only to
increase of efficiency and health in the individual but also to
possible effects on and improvements in the relationships of
man to man and on human culture in general.

We are familiar with various man-made machines and instruments which possess certain devices for the government or the
control of the operation of the mechanism as a whole. The
automobile is an example. Although this vehicle moves under
its own power, it is not self-directing, but the direction and
the rate of motion of its wheels are determined by devices
employed by the driver. These devices are often called the
"controls" of the car, and their presence suggests that we look
for analogs in the human mechanism, while remaining fully
aware of the many differences.

Corresponding to the wheels of the car are the muscle tissues in man. Just as motion of the car depends directly on the revolution of the wheels, whatever the motive force, so action of the human organism as a unit depends, as a rule, directly on the shortening and the lengthening of muscle fibers. Effort includes the shortening of muscle fibers, while relaxation is their lengthening. By these means alone man can move and effect diverse changes both in his environment and in himself, in accordance with the first law of Newton—which applies, likewise, to the motions of the automobile.

To be sure, the wheels of the car fail to turn unless the motor operates appropriately. It is equally true that the muscle tissues in intact man fail to contract and relax unless the afferent and the efferent nerve supplies—and, indeed, the entire nervous system—operate appropriately. However, since operations in any portion of the nervous system (nerve impulses) commonly occur without change of position in any section thereof, it is evident that neither the brain nor the nervous system is analogous to the wheels of the automobile; neither can be held immediately responsible for effecting action of the whole or of parts of the organism.

Engineering for Efficiency

The ratio of the work necessary to operate the controls of an automobile to the work performed by the wheels can be represented by the fraction C/E. Automotive engineers generally have directed their efforts toward making this fraction smaller with each year's model, partly by increasing the value of E but chiefly by lessening the value of C. Assuming that evolution tends in the same direction, we should expect in man an extremely small value for C. Because of the slight energies involved, the very existence of C might be overlooked.

If the varying stages of evolutionary development attained by organisms of different species and genera are represented by corresponding fractions C/E, a rough conception may be secured of the work-gain attained in each instance. In the mastodon, the value of E evidently became extraordinarily large.

Evolutionary history indicates the failure of such organisms to survive, based on attainment of excessive values of this denominator. The greater success attained in the evolution of man can be represented more clearly if the fraction is inverted, making it E/C, which roughly indicates the efficiency of the mechanism of control. Just as automotive engineers found it best to limit the power delivered at the wheels, so evolutionary tendencies evidently have met with the most marked success in man, whose effector strength is far less than that which characterized the mastodon.

In man the ratio E/C has become relatively large, but most striking has been the *qualitative* change in the manifestations of E. Man is able to carry out many and varied types of activities in addition to the forward and backward locomotion characteristic of the automobile. Among these are abilities to see and imagine seeing, to hear and imagine hearing, to write and imagine writing, and to recall correspondingly. Evidently, in the course of evolution, E has become diversified into many functions accomplished through the shortening and the lengthening of muscle fibers which rotation of wheels could not effect. As will be illustrated subsequently, the diversified abilities of man are derived from the favorable location of C— which is dispersed all over the exterior surface of his body beneath his skin rather than grouped exclusively in one location —as in the instance of the automobile, where they are located on the dashboard.* Thus, via the skeletal musculature, man can direct activities of his various parts due to devices which (1) indicate to him the nature and the magnitude of energy expenditure at any portion of his skeletal musculature and (2) enable him to initiate and direct the movement of his individual parts in a way that is obviously impossible for any instrument or machine constructed by man up to date.

When a switch or other mechanical device is operated by man, the control device is separated in space from the operator.

---

* C, representing controls in the muscle spindles, is within the effector (E) mechanisms, the striated muscles. Thus, both C and E are widely dispersed beneath the skin.

A different set of conditions exist when man operates autogenous controls, for here the control devices (motor nerves, muscle spindles) and the control indicators (muscle sensations) are not separable from the operator himself, but both operator and control devices and control indicators subsist in one and the same organism. To this extent man's employment of autogenous controls departs from strict analogy with his use of dashboard controls, for instance, in driving an automobile. (See Figs. 1 and 2, p. 59). There are a dozen other differences. Nevertheless, the comparison can be useful pedagogically, because driving has become a familiar pursuit and the error, if any, can be regarded as a constant error for which allowance can be made. Indeed, examples of departure from strict accuracy abound among scientific conceptions which, nevertheless, often prove to be useful not only practically but also for scientific understanding, provided that any error or deviation is duly noted and properly allowed for.

Control of Mental Operations

We must revise the concept traditional in medicine and psychiatry that the machinery of human ideation lies exclusively in the brain and other parts of the nervous system. It is necessary to consider that in no moment of ideation, emotion or other human activity does any nerve shorten or lengthen, however slightly, or engage in any structural change of location whatsoever. The brain and other nervous tissue are capable only of conducting electrochemical impulses; in themselves they are incompetent to effect direct mechanical (mobile) change internally or on the environment. It has been shown in this laboratory that mental operations, including imagination, recall and all forms of emotion, depend on specific operations of the skeletal (and other) musculature which, doubtless, are approximately simultaneous with (rather than subsequent to) hypothesized specific brain action. While locomotion of the organism or its parts involves muscular contractions which are readily recognized because they can be seen with the naked eye, mental operations involve muscular contractions which are not recognized readily because they are minuscule or micro-scopic. They require mechanical or electrical amplification for identification. Employing methods of action-potential measurement previously developed,* we now add evidence which indicates that, within certain limits, man is provided with psycho-physiologic functions such that through certain technical training he can acquire something like a driver's control of his organism and of various portions. (See Figs. 3 and 4, p. 59.) Such control depends in part on the muscle-sense which functions both with skeletal muscular contraction and with certain "servo" mechanisms, chiefly of visual character. Progressive relaxation—the negative phase of human self-direction—has been discussed.† Previous communications support the view that the self-direction of man can include his mental operations, insofar as these are determined by minute contractions of the eyes, the organs of speech and/or of other parts specifically involved in each mental act.

In no sense does this imply that the nervous system is unnecessary for reflection or, even, for locomotion. If we needed any evidence against this view, which we do not, the incapacity of children born anencephalic would be conclusive. They lie helplessly, owing to locomotor disability. The present principle is only that in certain views which have become traditional, functions which only muscle tissues could carry out have been vaguely attributed to nervous tissue, thus hindering the progress of psychiatry and other sciences related to the nature of human action.

To clarify what has been said above, let us ask just what may healthy and diseased individuals derive from the technical

* Jacobson, E.: The neurovoltmeter, Am. J. Psychol. 52:620-624, 1939; The direct measurement of nervous and muscular states with the integrating neuro-voltmeter, Am. J. Psychiat. 97:513-523, 1940; An integrating voltmeter for the study of nerve and muscle potentials, Rev. Sci. Instruments 11:415-418, 1940; Recording action-potentials without photography, Am. J. Psychol. 54:266-269, 1941. Jacobson, E., and Kraft, F. L.: Contraction potentials in man during reading, Am. J. Physiol. 137:1-5, 1952; The cultivation of physiological relaxation, Ann. Int. Med. 19:965-972, 1943.

† Jacobson, Edmund: Progressive Relaxation, revised ed., Chicago, University of Chicago Press, 1938.

training in running their organisms? After learning the new technics and making them habitual, how may their daily living performance differ? To answer these questions requires that we first outline the ordinary modes of behavior of persons who have never received training in the present sense.

Instinctual and Goal Living

That almost every act of man is to a certain extent determined by instinctual impulses can be said to be universally recognized. Thus, many or most of the occupations of the day, including eating, walking, talking, exercising and so forth, are built around instinctual acts involving the various senses and the reflexes. These few sentences about instinctual activities could, of course, be expanded into volumes, particularly in regard to reviews of the interplay of instincts, the developments of habit and the influence of environmental states, as shown by countless investigators.

Another basic source of human behavior may be called *goal living*. By this term I refer to the ability of man to set innumerable short-term and long-term goals for himself so that life as he recognizes it is largely the achieving of goals. For example, in Western cultures the modern worker has goals which include bathing, dressing and eating breakfast in the morning, later to be followed by goals variable with each individual as the day progresses. There are variable goals for the hour, the day, the week, the month, the year and for life. In brief, his manner of living, including his state of health at any time, is commonly determined not only by instincts and habits (and these, in turn, by body chemistry, the results of interplay of hereditary factors with environmental influences) but also by his innumerable goals.

It is important for the doctor to realize what is meant by goal living, including the phraseology employed here. The point to be emphasized is that goal living—the common form of everyday life—has a mechanical or physiologic side which never has been realized, much less investigated.* If now we continue our comparison of learning to run the human organism with learning to run an automobile, we can represent goal driving as something which nature has achieved in man but which automobile manufacturers have not yet attempted in cars. Perhaps some day cars may be built that apparently find their own way to any destination the rider chooses. Precisely this sort of thing is what nature has accomplished in man, who visualizes or otherwise represents a goal and then proceeds toward it, scarcely knowing by what mechanism or at what costs of energy.

Human Inefficiency

Because of this ignorance concerning his own mechanisms, I believe, man often displays lack of (mechanical) efficiency in his daily pursuits; and, not knowing how to count the costs of achieving his goals (in terms of muscular sensation denoting his efforts), he often runs his organism into overtense states— not only of the heart and the arterial systems. Thus, learning to drive the organism includes the ability to count the costs (by observation of states of muscular tension) and to distinguish between goals and tension-attitudes of the moment. However, it does not exclude other modes of living, whether instinctive or acquired, but modifies and supplements these in a new integration. Persons trained according to the new principles behave as naturally as do their untrained associates, but only up to the point at which the cost in terms of their energy reserves seems to them excessive. In this respect, they apply their learned skills toward making their reactions fit the situation.

Mechanical Controls

There are many types of governing devices or controls within the living organism. Among these are chemical and hormonal

---

* Psychologists have recognized goals clearly, beginning with the epoch-making studies of Watt, Ach, Messer and others of the Wuerzberger School. Their terminology has differed: namely, they used the expression *Aufgabe,* where I employ the word *goal.* Furthermore, they did not conceive the organism as being driven in terms of Aufgabe but spoke only of "determining tendencies" exciting subsequent mental activities.

substances in the tissues or the circulation which stimulate or limit specific operations within the organism. The brain and the nervous system are organized largely as an extremely complicated network of such devices, operating by the passage of electrochemical waves at speeds on the order of 5 to 100 meters per second. These devices of control are more or less arranged in various levels, as Hughlings Jackson pointed out, so that now we may appropriately speak of certain *controls of controls.* Among the latter types of controls are those which recently have been classified in the field of study entitled *cybernetics.* The numerous and profitable researches by investigators in every branch of physiology have disclosed how many and various are the types of internal controls which are engaged in every instant of the activity of the human and other animal organism. Their findings furnish a firm foundation for the position set forth here and lend it meaning.

However, what we discuss here is not "cybernetics" or the innumerable nervous, hormonal, chemical and other devices of control of specific activities within the organism (which constitute much of the subject of physiology and which engineers would call "automatic controls") but, rather, how individuals can learn to operate their muscular mechanisms to better advantage. Thus, we arrive at an engineering problem in human physics.

Teaching Self-Operations Control

This has been an everyday question both with patients and with normal individuals in the Jacobson Clinic. The teaching methods of self-operations control are a further development of those employed in the cultivation of progressive relaxation, described previously. It is doubtful that anyone can appreciate them fully from a written description, since direct experience is essential, as in any other laboratory procedure. For initial instruction, the subject, who has been lying on his back with eyes closed, bends his left hand back at the wrist, carefully noting the sensory experience in the wrist and the volar surface of the forearm, which are known as *strain sensations.*

When he successfully distinguishes between these strains and the sensations in the active extensor muscles, it is agreed tentatively to call the latter experience the *control* sensation. He can confirm the propriety of this nomenclature, in his own experience at least, by noting what he does if he exerts increasing power against the retarding hand of the instructor which restricts his arm movement at the wrist. As he performs these acts, the action-potential patterns may be set before him on an oscilloscope screen. If electrodes have been inserted into extensor muscles involved, he can observe the evidences of his muscular contraction or effort and can note also to what extent he succeeds in relaxing the extensor muscles. When he is requested to double the power which he is exerting, he can note that he uses his controls somewhat in the same manner as he directs movements of a motor car by the operation of controls on the dashboard. To be sure, the analogy, is far from complete, but it can prove a useful pedagogic comparison. The pedagogy must be in stages: as learning to spell is only a first step toward reading or writing, so the practices included in early instruction can be only preliminary to the controlled action which is the ultimate goal. In Chapter 5 I shall illustrate the practices and the principles of control of the organism as an entirety. As indicated above, the powers of the organism can be "on" or "off" by direct control, a function distinguishable from so-called association—well known to psychologists—and from conditioned and unconditioned reflexes—well known, also, to physiologists.

After beginning as indicated above, the individual can be instructed similarly in the control of the "on and off" action of each of the principal muscle groups of his organism. Such instruction may be given briefly in a course of 20 periods of 1 hour each or more fully in five to ten times this number, as occasion requires. In addition, as in the learning of any other skill, the patient needs to practice by himself. It is requisite that he be taught to distinguish the *control sensation* which derives from the muscle-sense of Bell from other types of sensation; that he learn to detect this control as an element present in the subjective experience of mental activities, including imagination, recollection and emotion; and that he acquire the habit of using this control in his daily living. To this end he needs to be trained to observe his own processes of sensation when he is facing daily problems and making adjustments to environment. It is imperative that he become accustomed to distinguish the controls (which he is learning to observe as sensations but also to use practically) from the problem which he tries to solve. The instruction may be worded: "Distinguish between issue and tension-attitude!" Thus, he may progress to the point at which he recognizes that even fears and anxiety states include a measure of his own efforts to meet the environment and, accordingly, can be rendered more subject to daily control.

Development of Electroneuromyometry

As indicated above, the direct control of neuromuscular power can be rendered graphically by means of an appropriate amplifier-oscilloscope assembly. These changes can be followed objectively by the subject and the instructor at the same time. Neuromuscular television requires stability of the circuit employed, but, if the action-potentials occur with grossly visible movements, they are readily recorded and no extraordinary sensitive apparatus is necessary. However, if the subject is to observe and the operator is to determine the onset and the decline of the control of imagination, recall and other types of mental activities, the voltage sensitivity needs to be on the order of several centimeters for a single microvolt applied across the input of the amplifier. Prerequisite are various control tests which have been described previously.*

To determine, locate and measure the neuromuscular action-potentials which indicate the tensions of the patient for the physiologic psychiatrist, I have developed the methods of electroneuromyometry. These are serviceable to the psychiatrist

---

* Jacobson, E.: Muscular tension and the smoking of cigarettes, Am. J. Psychol. 36:561-562, 1943.

as electrocardiographic methods are serviceable to the internist. I found it necessary to devise and to develop a type of instrument never before employed, with extreme voltage sensitivity and unusual stability. In this, for circuit design, I was fortunate in having the aid of engineers of the Bell Telephone Laboratories. More will be recounted in a later chapter.

Self-operations Control versus Conditioned Reflex

Traditional psychology deals with the association of ideas or of experiences, while the Pavlovian physiology approaches the learning processes more objectively, that is, without recourse to subjective reports from the human subject. In the instance of animal subjects, such reports, of course, cannot be secured. Much has been learned by thousands of investigators in these scientific but limited branches. However, it is necessary to emphasize that, when an association has been formed or when a conditioned reflex has been established, the result is a more or less *automatic* determination of certain neuromuscular activity on the occurrence of appropriate stimulation. This result derives from corresponding modifications (presumably, to some extent structural) in connections within the nervous system. However, the ability of the organism to learn to operate controls for the direction of its own activities results from the presence of structures in the muscle spindles which instigate muscular contracting and which, in turn, have been shown to be under cerebral control.* This ability, I have shown, can be further cultivated to an extraordinary extent. It would be stretching the meaning of the word to call such cultivation merely a special conditioning.

Learning the Technic

Cultivation of such ability depends on (a) sufficient repetition of observation of the control process by the subject and (b) sufficient repetition of the act of control in a positive or negative direction in each principle neuromuscular locale. The

---

* See Chapter 4, pp. 35-36.

physiology involved concerns relationships between functions of the cerebrospinal and the vegetative nervous systems.*

In training methods called Progressive Relaxation, the patient learns to recognize states of tension (contraction) in the chief skeletal muscular regions of the body and to relax them generally when lying at rest or differentially when in action. The pedagogy in the method of Self-Operation Control differs considerably in that the patient (as previously outlined) is trained to operate his organism as he would an instrument. He learns literally to go on and off with the power in the various sections of his organism, quickly or slowly but more thoroughly, as different occasions may require for efficiency.

Results

When this ability has been cultivated, a distinctly different type of reaction to environment becomes possible. His responses become less determined by fixed associations or habitual conditioning. His emotions become subject to a certain measure of control. He can work with less neuromuscular tension. He can be taught to distinguish between issue and attitude—between the problem which he faces and his own neuromuscular actions. The latter constitute his effort reaction while the former come to be regarded as the abstraction which they really are.

Need for Self-Operations Control

The healthy as well as the psychoneurotic person may desire to conserve the energies which he puts forth in his daily endeavors without lessening his productivity. This can be regarded as comparable with the desire to increase the efficiency of engines constructed by man. Opportunities to conserve energies arise in the daily life of most people in the present era, since, characteristically, they spend an inordinate amount of time and energy in what I shall call *evaluation*. It is imperative for successful living that each man evaluate situa-

---

* Jacobson, Edmund: Progressive Relaxation, revised, Chicago, University of Chicago Press, 1938.

tions—the reality which confronts him as well as what is in prospect; but there can be too much of a good thing.

Uncontrolled Chronic Anxiety

Chronic anxiety states consist to a great extent of prolonged, unnecessary and costly evaluation-efforts. It is of utmost importance to teach each overanxious patient to realize what he is doing; to observe his tension signals and to relax the tensions of excessive evaluation. In this he will never succeed until he learns self-honesty. Otherwise, he will give himself good reasons and excuses for his anxiety. He will point out his difficulties and emphasize that his worrying is justified—that life's problems must be solved, or the result will be catastrophe. There will be so much truth in this claim that it must be acknowledged by the instructor in tension control. At the same time, he faces the dilemma that the untrained individual will never learn to cope efficiently with anxiety states until he learns that his claim represents no more than a half-truth. Actually, he fails to distinguish his anxiety-tensions from the objective difficulties which he encounters. This distinction must be clear to the physician; otherwise he will be guilty of the "stimulus error" which E. B. Titchener and other experimental psychologists often pointed out to their students in normal psychology.

Instruction of the patient is required until he learns to make this scientific distinction. Only then will he really become effective in employing methods of self-operations control to conditions of anxiety. He will need drill in finding the processes at any moment of anxiety, namely, the tensions and the images which represent the situation to and in him. These anxiety tensions need to be recognized precisely as he would need to recognize the control devices on the dashboard of his motor car in order to drive it. After recognition, he must learn relaxation-control of these tensions, *regardless of whether his anxiety is or is not justified* by the severity and the stress of events.

Until he learns to do this successfully, he will never become fully able to control anxious states. Instructors in this field will note that it is a hard lesson to learn. As a means of instruction, suggestive and autosuggestive therapy will only hinder, not help. The instruction should be worded: "In anxiety conditions, you are to learn to distinguish the tensions from the objective difficult situation or problem which confronts you or is in prospect. After so doing, as a second step, you are to find and diminish the tensions and the images which you employ to represent your difficulties. Following this necessary preparation, as a third step, you are to begin to relax the tensions present which carry your anxiety for you. Most important of all, you are to learn to relax these tensions whether or not they are actually justified by the objective situation."

Daily Practice

The learner will need to practice as in learning any other skill. This practice will be required not only in hourly periods devoted to the purpose but also when he is active during his daily pursuits. He should be warned to look for repeated failure, as in the learning of any other new skill. No reassurance should be given as such that he is bound to succeed. Such reassurance will cramp his style. However, he should be informed that faith and self-confidence are unnecessary. He is to try and to try again, notwithstanding repeated failure, because the anxiety tensions are basically his own striving for purposes of solving his problems. Physiologically, therefore, he can act as if he is in a position to relax these tensions even at moments when he is sure that he cannot—a conviction that results naturally from previous failures. Often I inform the learner that I myself have learned most about the proposed technic at times when I have felt certain that, on this occasion, I would fail. On repeated attempts to relax the tension state, success often amazed me and taught me that the learner needs persistence more than confidence. To be sure, skill in any art eventually begets confidence, which, thereupon, can prove of help.

"Wear and Tear" Reduced

Thus, efforts are freed to operate in the real interest of the organism and there can be greater efficiency, which implies less pathologic wear and tear. This is because effort on the part of the organism, i.e., neuromuscular activity, evidently corresponds with usage of any instrument. With self-operations control as with progressive relaxation, both systolic and diastolic pressure commonly tend to lower values. This is generally true not only in patients with essential hypertension but in individuals with normal blood pressure levels as well. Tension reactions in turn are dependent on the blood pressure and the circulation. Accordingly, skeletal muscular contraction requires increased work of the heart and, especially, also, of the smooth musculature of the arterioles. Notwithstanding the amazing measures of tissue restoration and repair characteristic in the organism, we may assume that excessive effort tends precipitately or in the long run toward organic disruption and senile change.

Tensions Differ From Selye "Stress"

The life of man consists largely of efforts and subefforts. We should not confuse the effects of daily efforts with what is currently known as *stress*, including the alarm reaction of Hans Selye. Much valuable information has been gained about glandular and steroid chemical responses to certain types of change in the environment. However, it should be noted that the alarm reaction to stress is an unusual rather than an everyday occurrence in man; while the exertion of effort occurs every moment and constitutes much of his life. The former is due to operation of mechanical controls in the organism, which are the subject matter of animal physiology. Our efforts are a different matter.

The vast expansion of the medical sciences together with intensive specialization have resulted in neglect of the physiology of effortful adaptation. Yet we know that every muscular contraction requires oxygen and glycogen for the combustive processes and requires equally the removal of waste products, including carbon dioxide, lactic acid, pyruvic acid and mineral ash. These requirements can be satisfied only through appropriately increased operations of the cardiovascular apparatus. Thus, a life of excessive effort and strain can be expected to show overactivity of the cardiovascular system in one form or another, with possible ultimate pathology.

Tension Disorders

In the approach to neurotensive disorders, which often are accompanied by hypertension, it does not appear sufficient to rely only on barbiturates and other measures of sedation, including psychotherapy, or on other medications such as cyanates, sympatholytic and ganglionic blocking drugs or even on palliative measures of salt restriction or surgery. From what we are beginning to learn about the efforts of man in his daily adjustments to his environment and their long-time effects when they are excessive, it would appear that man is subject to a variety of ills which can be termed Tension Disorders or Diseases of Self-Activation. Medication, surgery or psychotherapy may in different ways alleviate the *symptomatic* manifestations of such diseases without penetrating to the source of the mischief, if this really lies in waste of human effort. Suggestions that the patient engage in hobbies, or move to another environment or change his philosophy have failed notoriously to remove the basic cause. Whether pathologic alterations have become irreversible or not, technical advances here outlined now provide measures of teaching the patient to avoid waste of effort in meeting his daily obligations.

Man has lived largely in terms of his instincts and emotions—less often in terms of his reason. Hitherto, the "life of reason" has been universally regarded as the most effective mode. To this we can no longer wholly concur. The measures herein outlined differ not in being less rational but in being practical and clinical. Our measures are not merely philosophic or popular. Man, we suggest, has failed to distinguish the situations and the issues which he faces from his own activation patterns. Only when he becomes able to recognize his own psychophysiologic patterns and to distinguish them from environmental problems, does the door open for a change in his living.

Why Self-Operations Control Has Been Overlooked

If it is valid and useful to regard man as thus potentially a self-driving unit provided with controls as well as effectors in the neuromuscular system, which he can learn to operate for his own individual purposes in adjusting to environment, why has this fact been overlooked hitherto? Among assignable reasons, one stands out clearly. Man is accustomed to running the controls of automobiles, planes and other constructed devices which lack a feature that distinguishes his own nervous system; in them, when a particular control is repeatedly applied under similar conditions, it does not tend to become semi-automatic in operation as it does in man. To visualize such a device, one may recall the hand-operated "choke" with which the automobile in the late thirties was equipped to control the richness of the gasoline mixture on cold days; if, after repeated use of this device by hand, the "choke" began to adjust itself when needed, the development of mechanisms in the automobile would parallel with those which underlie habit formation and conditioned reflexes in man. However, no such device has ever been developed by man and employed in his mechanical contrivances. It would be a totally new experience if, after operating a control by hand repeatedly, the control began to work by itself. We assume that the possibility of man learning to drive his own organism via technical instructions has been overlooked in medicine and the humanities because of this significant difference between the biologic and the man-made controls and their operation.

Effort Control and Adaptation

Effective effort control means better adaptation to environment; it can tend toward greater efficiency in every occupation of man. Activity, including reflection, can make less demands upon the cardiovascular apparatus. As stated above, the blood pressure commonly tends to be lowered, not only in normal subjects but also in many hypertensives. Theoretically, the incidence of coronary heart disease should be significantly diminished in groups of persons properly trained in control methods.* Likewise, as previously set forth, the incidence of spastic states of the alimentary tract which characteristically accompany neurotensive states, including those which apparently lead in the direction of peptic ulcer, should be diminished.

Accordingly, the principles of tension control can be applied widely in medical sciences and practice. Neuropsychiatric disorders and the tension disorders treated by the internist commonly occur in one and the same patient concurrently or successively. Maladies which deserve to be known as tension disorders commonly occur in one and the same patient concurrently or successively, whether recognized or not. Specialists classify these maladies as belonging in the field of the neuropsychiatrist, the internist, etc., but Nature has made no such distinction. In consequence, internists generally include among their clientele many patients with neuropsychiatric symptoms and neuropsychiatrists treat many patients with symptoms of gastrointestinal and other organic mulfunction.

Preventive Medicine

In both specialties, tension control might be applied not only in the treatment but also the prevention of disease. Among other objectives, according to the principles outlined, it seems possible that, in an adequately trained population, the present high death rate from cardiovascular disease could be more effectively controlled. As in other divisions in regard to social welfare, preventive medicine may prove to be more important than the effective treatment of disease. In preventive medicine, autokinetic methods should promise no "cure" to the individual who seeks specialized education, any more than the student who registers in school is promised success in his education by the instructors. If the methods of effort education can be made available to the general populace, prevention and, to some extent, cure of the diseases of self-activation may become possi-

---

* Jacobson, Edmund: Principles underlying coronary heart disease (considerations for a working hypothesis), Cardiologia 26:83-102, 1955.

ble—but only provided that the responsibility for carrying out instructions be placed where it belongs, namely, squarely on the individual himself.

Summary

Man has autogenous controls which, to some extent, operate unawaredly and instinctively but which he can learn to recognize. He can be taught definitely to operate his organism as he is taught to operate man-made instruments and semi-automatic vehicles. Physiologic controls are available which correspond in many respects with dashboard controls in the automobile, for example (as muscle fiber contraction evidently corresponds with wheel revolution). Important differences derive from the fact that in man the control mechanisms are self-operated, whereas, in the automobile and most other man-made instruments, the driver is external. However, evidence suggests that cultivated habitual use of controls can improve adaptation to modern environment, including personal efficiency and relations between men. Under modern pressures, unawareness and consequent failure to employ these controls evidently leads to neuromuscular overactivity with energy waste; this, apparently, has been partly responsible for the most common of diseases, namely, tension disorders or the diseases of self-activation, including many fatigue states, neurotic conditions, peptic ulcer, irritable colon and, often, hypertensive disorders including coronary heart disease. Physicians differ endlessly in the many and various forms of treatment to be administered in these conditions, including medicines, diet, surgery, removal from irritating environment and conventional psychotherapy, but, notoriously, the treatment generally proves to be only palliative at best and new symptoms soon set in. Evidently because these diverse varieties of treatment all fail to penetrate to the basic cause, the diseases of self-activation continue in millions of instances, constituting a sort of modern plague. The evidence suggests that, however large the undertaking, a program of effective preventive medicine will require technical education for the populace in physiologic self-control.

CHAPTER **5**

How To Teach
Self-Operations
Control in Daily
Practice

In the preceding chapter we saw that man can be regarded
as a complex instrument and that, with proper training, he can
learn to run the instrument which is himself. This view of man
is new in science, and there are reasons to believe that it offers
a more realistic conception than do various other views that
have historical priority.

If, as scientists and doctors, we teach this view to our
patients, it is only fitting that we explain that the view entails
no criticism of other views. If they cherish the belief that man
is created in the image of God, they may continue to do so.
Again, if they devote their faith to the Christian doctrines of
sacrifice and resistance to temptation, they will find close
parallels to these doctrines in the scientific understanding of
human efficiency.

Indeed, the basic aim of self-operations control is no less
than the maintenance or the increase of human efficiency in
every phase of life. An economist has pointed out that, in the
last analysis, all wealth results from abstinence. Self-operations

control is founded on the same principle. Its aim is the conservation of muscular energy linked with optimum accomplishment of daily purposes.

Muscular energy is basically chemical. It has to do with high phosphate bonds in muscle, particularly in the form of adenosinetriphosphate. Evidence suggests that creatine phosphate is the key and that, if this falls as low as 40 milligrams per cent, there is fatigue and the muscle lacks the wherewithal to relax.

Consequences of Disregard of Energy Expenditure

No businessman would open a store for sales, expecting to take into account income alone, with no tab on expenses. Yet this is the way we live commonly. We neglect our muscle energy expenditures, although muscle tissue constitutes about half the weight of the entire body and although every one of our efforts all day long constitutes an energy expenditure. This energy expenditure is the cost of tensing our muscles and, also, of relaxing them in the complex and individuated patterns which make up our daily lives.

Life, as man leads it, at best is expensive of our vital energies. At worst, it involves much needless waste. How to avert such waste, at least to some extent, can be taught by the doctor interested in self-operations control. Fortunately, he can learn much himself through teaching, and, eventually, this can aid him in his own daily life under high pressures. Thus, both doctor and patient can share the interest in learning to live more efficiently.

Indeed, as said previously, what is the underlying purpose of all medical practice, including surgery and the specialties, if not in the maintenance or the increase of personal efficiency? What doctor would remove an ailing appendix, what dentist an ailing tooth unless this enabled the patient to maintain or increase his daily accomplishment or efficiency? Such have been the basic if unrecognized aims of all forms of scientific medicine in the past. These can be compared with repair of our motor cars in shops set up for that purpose.

But what of driving? Medicine has neglected this to a large extent. But medicine can come to its maturity in the present decade by introducing to the patient the need and the means of driving his own organism scientifically. Medicine must also provide drill, for no one learns to drive a car or run an instrument without instruction and practice toward the attainment of habitual skill.

Special Responsibilities of the Doctor and the Patient

These considerations in one form or another can be conveyed to the patient in preamble. Also, it should be emphasized that when the doctor teaches medically, he assumes responsibility different from that involved in his traditional practice in diagnosis and treatment, whether it be medicine, surgery or any one of the other specialties, including psychiatry. To be sure, he takes the responsibility for the diagnosis that his patient needs to learn self-operations control for the alleviation or the cure of malady. But no teacher can assume responsibility for what his pupil will do in carrying out a skill according to his individual learning powers. Sometimes I say to my patient, "You will be on your own. I can show you how to drive a car, but the responsibility when you drive will be on your shoulders! If you ask me for reassurance that you will learn to relax, my reply is that your request is out of place. You would not demand that the dean of any school guarantee that you will become a good pupil. There, as here, the responsibility should and must be yours!"

Following this kind of preamble, the doctor may in his own words add something on the following order:

To give some idea of what we are setting out to do, the human organism may be compared with the automobile. Let me remind you that the essential parts of an automobile are the wheels. These circular bodies move along the ground. Owing to friction and a one-one correspondence between parts of the wheel and parts of the ground, the wheels turn and cause the car to go in the direction that the driver desires. But quite as essential also to the car are the controls on the dashboard.

First of all, let me show you that part of our organisms corresponds to the wheels of the motor car. As you know, the removal of a single wheel would render the car useless. Now, what part of you corresponds to the wheel? Is it your skin? Certainly not; your skin is largely only a protective covering. Is it the fatty tissue? Certainly not, because that tissue, as you know, is largely inert. Is it the bones? Certainly not. The bones are merely pulled or pushed along passively. Is it the connective tissues which form scars? This connective tissue moves a little, but not much. It certainly is not what, in you, corresponds to the wheels. Is it the blood? This moves, but it, also, is merely pushed along. "Aha," you say, "I know exactly what corresponds to the wheels. The brain! The nervous system!" And they certainly do not! After all, the wheels are the parts of the automobile which permit it to change its position in space according to the first law of Newton, force = mass × acceleration. The nervous system and the brain do not move one hundredth of an inch in exercising their functions. There is no correspondence.

The brain and the nervous system are comparable with a vast system of telephone wires. As a matter of fact, the system in each one of you is as complicated as the entire telephone system of the United States. Over your nerve fibers and cells course impulses. They do not travel as fast as electrical charges over the telephone wires, which move with the speed of light. The impulses that go along your nerve fibers, travel at rates, much lower, such as 40 meters per second. This is an electro-chemical process. But, in the discharge of its function, neither the brain nor the nervous system moves in the slightest; obviously, there is no capacity in the brain or the nervous system in themselves to enable you to change your environment, which means in plain, practical terms, carrying on your daily affairs.

What, then, is the effector organ? It is the muscle tissue. In your muscle tissue you have your wheels. Muscle tissue is composed of little fibers often so thin that you cannot see them;

often no longer than about two inches. Those fibers shorten and lengthen; that is nature's substitute for wheels. Or shall we say that man invented wheels as a substitute for the contraction and the lengthening of muscle fibers?

Everything you accomplish, everything you do all day long consists in part of the shortening and the lengthening of muscle fibers. You sit down at your desk in the morning and you write a note. You pick up your telephone. These, as well as any other acts which you perform, consist of patterns of varying complexity, shortening and lengthening of fibers in the arm muscles, the chest muscles, the eye, the tongue, the organs of speech. Throughout every activity in which you engage from morning till night, there is one fundamental note. This is the shortening and the lengthening of muscle fibers. You live in these terms.

If shortening and lengthening the muscle fibers is what corresponds to the turning of wheels in the car, our next inquiry is, how is this to be controlled? Your motor car has a starter button, an ignition device, a clutch or a fluid drive and a brake. Let us agree to call all those things "controls" of the car which you operate. How is the shortening and the lengthening of muscle fibers to be controlled? Let me put the matter more practically. If in this course I can show you how to control the shortening and the lengthening of your muscle fibers a little better, you will really have the keynote to the running of your organism. The purpose of this project is to teach the individual how to run his organism in the same sense that he learns to run an automobile. It is to teach him what you might call self-control—but not, of course, in a moral sense. The control of the organism is to be understood in the same sense as the control of the automobile. You can drive to where you want to go. This becomes as technical as teaching someone how to drive a car.

From one point of view, the objectives of the manufacturers of automobiles can be stated in the following terms: They aim to decrease the amount of work the driver has to do to run a car and for the most part, to increase the power at the wheels.

If you express this as a fraction, you would have C as a numerator and E as the denominator, and the job of the automobile manufacturer is to make the fraction C/E as small as possible. Thus, he would make the effort of the driver in running the car as little as possible, while the power delivered at the wheels should be made as great as possible.

Automobile manufacturers have been in business for about 60 years and have done a good job. But nature has been in business longer. Longer than 60 thousand years—longer, perhaps, than 60 million years. The objectives of nature and the manufacturers may be said to be largely the same. Nature has made the controls very easy to operate. In fact, she has done the job so well that people have not really recognized that they have controls. They have overlooked them, and, therefore, one of the tasks of this course will be to instruct you to find those controls.

Nature has not simply concealed the controls; what she has done is to make them require a very small amount of energy to operate. Because very little energy is required to operate what can be employed as controls for the life of man, mankind has overlooked them.

We become very familiar with certain types of controls. There is a little switch; you press it and the lights go on or off. But if you were to call in a native from mid-Africa and show him how to operate the light control, he might regard it as magic and think of you as a magician. If you ask him to put out the light, he might try to do so by throwing something at the light.

Likewise, mankind has not observed his controls; he has operated on a basis of habit, emotion or instinct. But he must become a little more mature; he must take into account that he is operating a very complex mechanism in his daily affairs— a mechanism far more complex than an automobile and one which, for best usage, requires a certain skill on his part.

If you are an average person, you carry your problems home with you and you are tense. There is too much contraction of muscle fibers, and the consequences are that the heart is strained unduly and you have coronary heart disease or the high blood pressure which results from being tense or the low blood pressure which results from fatigue. Please do not misunderstand me. Every one of these disorders that I have mentioned has more than one particular cause. The cause of high blood pressure cannot be stated to be excess tension alone. But if you will be kind enough to remember what I said, I believe that the matter will be clear in its implication.

Permit me once more to compare the matter with the driving of an automobile. A car with banged up fenders and radiator is brought to a shop for repair, and the repair is made. Three months later, the car is back—this time, perhaps, it is the rear and the front doors or the rear bumper that has been damaged. Once more, the repair is made. If this keeps up, it finally may become apparent to the driver or the repairman that what this automobile owner needs most is better driving. Similarly, high blood pressure or coronary heart disease doubtless depends on many factors, and some of those factors are doubtless hereditary. The individual is born with such tendencies. However, to carry the automobile analogy a little further, if you have a defective tire and you cannot change it (as, unfortunately, you have no opportunity to exchange your arteries for new ones), what should you do? You should learn to drive with a defective tire. Learn to drive that car so that it will last longer! If you learn to drive carefully, you may prolong your car's usefulness. Your car may outlive other cars which are driven carelessly even though they originally were provided with better tires. What I am trying to indicate is not that tension is the one and only cause of disease—for that would be an entire misapprehension of what I am saying—but that we deal here with the total organism. We deal here with the management of that organism, which, well or defective, can still be driven for better or for worse.

Let us repeat that everything the individual does from morning till night consists of the shortening and the lengthening of muscle fibers. To a certain extent, nature has arranged that many of those contractions are more or less automatically induced. For example, an individual suddenly sees a curtain of flame and becomes tense. He does not need to run his organism to say "Now I need to be tense!" There is an automatic induction of much of this shortening of muscle fibers, but that automatic induction is frequently excessive. If the curtain is aflame, there is occasion for the individual to be somewhat tense—to be prepared to put it out or call the fire department. But, if he is excessively tense, he interferes with his own efficiency, and there rises the need of training for better control.

I have described the general purposes of our plan of instruction as having to do with control of the organism. This, of course, means the going on of power as well as the going off of power. The going off of power is relaxation. Since there is no magic that would enable me to show you in 15 minutes how to be controlled in going off with your powers, instruction has to be by steps through one muscle group after another and new habits need to be formed. I shall have much to say about this to you in the individual periods of instruction. What I want to emphasize now is that in this course of instruction our task will be more than to show you how to go off with the power— how to relax—which is the negative aspect.

When an individual is shown how to go off with his power, it is necessary to show him how to do it quickly, and, to a certain extent, skill can be acquired so that individuals learn to go off with that power in small fractions of a second. But, ordinarily, the job is not complete when it is done so quickly. What is needed is a slower but more thorough procedure.

Here you have a wall switch which suddenly turns off this light. There is provided in the human organism a mechanism by which the power goes off gradually. This gradual decline is known as progressive relaxation.

You will wonder, what has this to do with the mind? It has everything to do with the mind. The mind is not something which is completely different from the physical organism, any more than digestion is something entirely different from the stomach and the esophagus and the colon. The mind is a function of the organism. However, the mind is not the function only of the nervous system and the brain. This was shown conclusively in the early 30's. In every mental operation there is a shortening and a lengthening of muscle fibers in various manners and procedures which you yourself will have a chance to observe in yourself. These findings, while not thoroughly understood, are now in the textbooks of experimental psychology which are used in the universities the world over. Many of the professors of psychology clearly realize that the mind is not, as formerly believed, a function only of the brain and the nervous system. The simplest evidence is that you find your mind getting quieter on the relaxation of certain muscles. If relaxation is carried sufficiently far, you will find yourself no longer engaged in concentration or thinking or emotion. A blank is attained on the relaxation of certain musculature. In contrast, when you imagine or reflect, you always tense muscles —commonly those of the eyes and of speech, but often including any others of the body.

Thus self-operations control applies to everything you do or can do. It includes the *mental* no less than the *physical*.

Operative Instructions (Recognition of Tension)

Period 1. Following the verbal instructions, the patient reclines on a couch in most courses. However, it is permissible to begin in the sitting posture instead. Better observation is secured when lying, but there are counter-advantages when sitting is employed at the outset. The patient becomes aware at once that scientific relaxation is not mostly for resting purposes.

The patient is to lie down on his back with his arms at his sides. He is told that he is to keep his eyes open for several minutes, after which he is to close his lids gradually in order to be able to observe delicate sensations accurately. While he does so the doctor may leave the room. The patient is to estimate the times mentioned and is not to bother to look at his wristwatch or any other timepiece. Once he has closed his eyes, he is to keep them closed during the entire hour, so as to be able to observe better. He is informed that few words will be spoken. He is to learn to observe and operate himself.

When the doctor has returned, he sits by the couch and requests the patient to bend his left hand back at the wrist. Perhaps he indicates the movement desired by example (letting the patient open his lids for a moment) or, better, by bending the hand back for the patient to hold steadily in that position.

Many beginners will bend to and fro, which may be called see-sawing. If this is done, the doctor tells the learner to bend back steadily, and not to see-saw.

While the patient is bending back his left hand, the doctor may speak as follows:

Although your eyes are closed, you know that you are bending back your left hand at the wrist. If I were to ask you how you know this, you might give the following reasons. Of course, you are to check on what I say.

"First, before I came back, you had been experiencing sensations in the undersurface of your left hand which you attributed to contact with the couch, but you no longer have these sensations. Instead, the feeling is as if the hand is in the air. Can you confirm this?" (The learner will nod or answer affirmatively as a rule.)

"Very well. But there is a second reason why you know that you are bending back your left hand, although you do not see it bending. As you bend back, you have the same sort of feeling at the wrist [indicating] as you have had in the past when your eyes were open and you could see your hand bending. The sensation has become associated with knowledge of the act. You have been so conditioned. Therefore, when you have this feeling at the wrist, you know that your hand is bending back. Is this true?" (The learner generally agrees, but may offer some comment.)

"Let us agree to call the feeling at the wrist by the name of *strain*. Wherever in the body you have a feeling kindred to this, we shall call it *strain*."

"If I bend your hand back thus [doing so], I can increase the strain felt. This suggests that strain is a passive experience.

Something is being done to you." (Patient agrees.) "Let us assume that the same is true also when you bend back at the wrist. The feeling of strain there, we may assume, is likewise passive only; you—not I, this time—are doing something the passive effects of which you feel at the wrist." (Patient agrees.)

"The strain at the wrist along with the absence of sensations of contact with the couch in the undersurface of the hand are two factors which enable you to know that you are bending back your hand at the wrist, even though your eyes remain closed."

"There is a third matter for you to observe. If you will notice carefully, you may perhaps sense here [indicating by light touch of the doctor's hand the upper surface of the left forearm] a very delicate sensation different in degree to what you have in the right forearm. Do you get it?"

Generally the answer is in the affirmative. If not, the patient continues to bend back his left hand while trying to recognize the sensation in the upper surface of the left forearm. He may cease to bend without being instructed to do so, whereupon the physician says, "Keep on bending, please." He may add that without doubt the patient really is experiencing the sensation, for, if he were devoid of it, he would not be able to use his arm in normal fashion. Persons who are born with a lack thereof (with Little's Disease) or who develop some malady which deprives them of the sensation fail to employ the limb with dexterity. The patient is informed that he is looking for too striking a sensation and will be disappointed. He should look for a delicate note. When gazing out of the window to detect a faint mist, he should not expect something "to hit him in the eye." He should be cautioned repeatedly that he has been looking for too much. Instead, he should look for a faint, delicate, pervasive sensation, more familiar to him than his own name. By this sensation he can recognize that his left forearm is active in a way that his right is not.

If the beginner still indicates that he is doubtful, he is instructed to cease bending and the doctor leaves the room to give him another opportunity to rest and, later, to try to

FIG. 1. In automobiles wheels are the effector mechanisms and are subject to control devices on or near the dashboard.

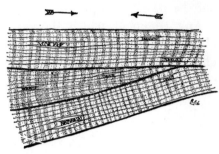

FIG. 2. In man, shortening muscle fibers are the effector mechanisms (subject to control devices in or near the muscles themselves).

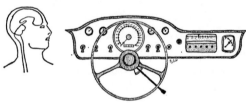

FIG. 3. The driver makes contact with external control devices. By employing these mechanical controls he can determine rate, direction and duration of car motion.

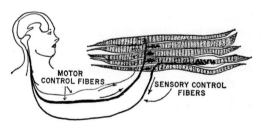

FIG. 4. The patient is in constant contact with internal control devices which he can be trained to observe and employ purposively. By employing these physiologic controls he can determine degree, location, extent and duration of the activity of the organism as a whole.

observe once more. This can be repeated at discretion, until the patient begins to appear definite or, at least, less doubtful.

It may seem necessary or helpful for the doctor to strengthen the sensation by offering passive resistance by his own hand, holding back the patient's hand during the bending. Once this has brought a positive response, the act can be repeated without the passive resistance.

Any comment which the doctor can make to encourage observation is in order, even if the pupil has responded affirmatively. If he seems to be a good observer, he may be encouraged to describe the qualities of the sensation, whether strong or faint, agreeable or disagreeable, diffuse or sharply outlined.

"This sensation in the upper surface of your left forearm," the physician may add, "is by agreement to be called the *control sensation*. We agree to call any sensation elsewhere in the body by the same name if it feels the same. You are to identify it by the character of the sensation.

"However, we do not assume that you will always be right when you try to identify it. On the contrary, we assume that, without training, you will often be wrong. Therefore, it will be necessary to train you to observe this sensation in its fine variations.

"At first, you may find yourself a little uncertain whether you really detect and identify it. What you need is to observe it repeatedly. With practice, you can become as adept as a coffee or wine taster. The sensation can grow on you. You can become able to detect it in one thousandth part of the strength of this experience, if only you give it your interest. If you are to learn to run your organism, you must observe the controls by which you can run your organism. You must learn not to ignore them even in the course of daily affairs which engross you.

"Bend back again and try to note the difference between this sensation and that of strain lower down, at the wrist. The strain, as you will note, is more readily distinguished, stands out a little more, appears to have a more definite character and bounds.

"The control sensation, we assume, is *you doing*. It is your effort. Note whether this appears to be true. The strain is not *you doing;* but seems to be passive in your immediate experience. The sensations of control and those of strain vaguely resemble each other, more than they resemble sounds or visual sensations. However, you can learn to discriminate between them readily. They are different sensations and the fibers which mediate them are in two different sections of the spinal cord.

"The same sensation which we agree to call the control from another point of view can be called the sensation from muscular tenseness—or tenseness, for short. If you desire, you can feel the muscle in the top of your left forearm as it hardens, giving you the sensation mentioned. By using the two terms last mentioned, you can refer to the literature on relaxation and progressive relaxation."

The doctor should not talk long at a time, else he will prevent the patient from relaxing. He may leave the room at intervals, leaving instructions so that the patient will not continue to repeat the tensions.

Defining Relaxation

The doctor should not use the words *relax* or *relaxation* until he has defined them. If the patient does so prematurely, the doctor may admonish him by saying, "We will come to that later on." He should carefully explain to the patient that as a team they are agreeing to use words precisely so that each will thereafter know what the other means.

On returning to the room after an interval allowed for rest, the patient is requested to bend his hands steadily back once more. Thereupon the doctor may say, "If we call this act your forearm *going positive,* what would we mean if you were to *go negative?* Now!"

Promptly, as a rule, this question is followed by relaxation of the muscles which extend the hand or, at least, the hand is returned to the couch through concomitant action of the flexors. In either event, the doctor should follow promptly with the question, "What happened to the control sensation when your hand went negative?"

If the answer is that the control sensation diminished or disappeared, this gives the doctor the opportunity to say, "Let us agree to call the elimination or the disappearance of the control sensation *relaxation*. Then, if you are right when you believe that it diminishes, you have with you at all times the ability to judge with technical accuracy whether you are really relaxed in a part. But for this we must agree to mean by relaxation the diminution not of sensations of strain, pain, tickle, touch, heat or cold or any other type but of muscular tension (the control sensation) alone.

If the patient appears adept, the term relaxation should be defined thus on relaxing following the very first occasion of bending back his hand. In all events, relaxation should be defined as early as the doctor finds possible.

The instruction to "go negative" is employed most often. Many will fail to do so, returning the part to its original position, instead, through the action of antagonistic muscles. Each occurrence of replacement should be noted on the relaxation record sheets for each patient.

After the patient has been permitted to go negative for a brief time he is requested to bend back the hand again. "This is your effort," he is told. "It is *you* doing, *you* working. But if you go negative, you are not to tense. An effort to relax is an effort like any other effort. It is work. It is not relaxing. Going negative will not be performed until you learn not to make an effort to do so. The one and only thing required is to go off with the power.

"People who never have been trained to relax commonly make efforts to do so. In this they are self-frustrated. They weary or exhaust themselves with repeated efforts. Imagine trying to stop slowly by pressing your foot down on the accelerator pedal! How impossible! This is one reason why many people untrained to relax tend to become increasingly nervous under conditions of hardship."

On some occasion when the patient is bending back his hand, he is informed further of the importance of learning to recognize the sensation from muscular tension. "No man-made instrument," he is told, "is similarly provided with gauges conveniently placed wherever energy is being spent so that the person who runs it can estimate the cost in energy spent. What a splendid device, if once you learn to use it. For your muscles are your traffic, your performers. There you spend your chief working energies. If you are to learn to conserve your energies, you must learn to estimate your expenditures. Learn to take advantage of this apparatus!"

In many instances, the patient will derive profit from seeing a diagram of muscle controls in the spindles (p. 59) and from comparing them with the controls on the dashboard of a car. This should be shown to him before or after a session of operational instructions.

When the doctor leaves the room, he should warn the patient that he is to maintain the relaxed state. "While I am out," he may say, "you are to remain negative. Do not bother to bend again or to do anything else. Take any noise I may make or any disturbance in my coming or going as a signal to remain negative or to relax all the more."

Practice, Not Exercise

It will be necessary to point out, perhaps repeatedly, that bending the hand back is *not* an exercise. Exercise is a muscular act designed to promote muscular strength, development and skill and to improve circulation. As the individual practices, he performs the exercise more vigorously. On the contrary, bending the hand back is *not* done for any of these purposes. Its sole purpose is to enable the observer to gain skill at noting the control sensation, the sensation from muscular contraction. As the patient practices this, instead of performing it more vigorously, he performs it with less and less contraction. He learns to recognize the sensation for muscular tension when the hand moves back about one tenth of a millimeter per second, which is actually not visible. Even more slight is the contraction in many persons when they merely imagine bending back the hand. It is necessary for the subject to learn to recognize just such very slight contractions. The purpose is to show him how to control his emotional states a little better.

The most vital aspects of relaxation training are misunderstood by anybody who identifies the purposes of the practices shown in the figures with "*exercises.*" It is frequently necessary to correct subjects who use this expression and it has seemed warranted to assume that they would not employ the incorrect expression if they really understood fully the purpose of the practices mentioned. As a rule, the doctor should take pains to suit the word to the action and to avoid misuse of any technical expression with the utmost care.

After the patient has recognized the control sensation on bending back the left hand, has relaxed for a few minutes and the doctor has returned, he bends his hand forward at the wrist. His hand should be at rest on the ulnar side. Thereupon he is asked to point to the present site of the control sensation.

If he misses, he is given further opportunities before the location is pointed out. On being requested to go negative, many or most persons restore their hands to the former position with a quick contraction. Some rotate the hand to the prone position. They should be given repeated opportunities to do better with or without telling them that they have made an effort.

If the length of time allotted to the entire course permits, enough has been accomplished for the first hour period. Otherwise, the operation of bending the left forearm at the elbow (arm 4) and even pressing down against the books (arm 5) may be included. If allotted time is short, the patient is shown how to relax the left arm progressively. Otherwise, practices arm 4 and arm 5 as well as arm 6 are given during subsequent periods.

Going Negative

Before showing the learner how to relax the entire left arm progressively it is well to explain the aim and procedure. "Unlike the wall-switch by which you turn the electric light on and off, we are provided with no device to turn off or to release muscular tension. Up to this time, you have been drilled in going off with the power quickly. It is advantageous to become skilled at quick relaxation, but electrical tests disclose that the quick let-go is often insufficient. When you put out a fire in a dry forest, you should extinguish the last spark. It is sometimes desirable to extinguish the last spark of the combustion in muscular contraction, and this is not ordinarily accomplished by quick relaxation. A slower but more thorough art should be learned as well.

"To teach you this, we shall use what I call an artifact. Think of advertisements or television, where the use of a carpet cleaner is demonstrated; but first the carpet is soiled with dirt purposely. The soiling is not part of the cleaning but is an artifact for demonstration purposes. Similarly, we first ask you to make your arm tense in a certain manner in order to permit you to relax it afterward. I explain all this to you to avoid any impression that the tension to be performed as a preliminary to relaxation is part of the relaxation procedure. It is not. The purpose of progressive relaxation of the entire arm is to do away with the last sparks of tension which remain, as a rule, after you relax your arm quickly.

Residual tension is the term applied to the tension which ordinarily remains when people lie down to relax. The purpose of progressive relaxation of the arm is to do away with residual tension.

"To do away with residual tension is of vast importance. A barrel of fluid which leaks only a drop or so per second will be found empty after a day; in the same way, residual tension is a constant drain on muscular energies of the untrained. What we need to do is to inculcate habits to stop this unnecessary drain."

At this point, while sitting by the couch, the doctor places the finger tips of one hand along the muscles of the upper arm and those of the other along the muscles of the forearm. "Will you begin to stiffen your entire arm, but ever so little. Gradually increase the tension, but very slowly. Make it increase gradually, ever so slightly—more and more."

If the patient proceeds irregularly, he is corrected and requested to begin again. He is to tense his arm slowly and progressively. When he has succeeded in this, he is instructed, "Whatever you have been doing up to this point, do so not quite so much. A little less and, again, a little less tension! Very gradually, relax slowly and progressively! No effort at all, please! Even after I leave the room, continue to go negative. If you feel no residual tension, nevertheless continue as you would if it were tense, setting yourself as if to go negative further and further each minute. You may be slightly tense still; you may assume that you still are slightly tense and, therefore, may continue on going negative as you were doing when you still detected tension."

The patient may be interested to learn that even the untrained frog possesses a brain mechanism for progressive relaxation. A frog kept in the dark in a favorable, damp atmosphere was found to relax progressively in a slow curve over a 50-minute period.

The possession of this brain mechanism by lower animals suggests that man may have it likewise, in some lower brain center. If so, to induce a man to relax progressively, it is necessary to set this mechanism in operation and free it from inhibitions. Perhaps this is what we accomplish by instructions such as those given above.

Successive periods of instruction are devoted to the muscle groups of the right arm. When the patient is requested to point with the fingers to the left arm where he notes the control sensation, a record is kept of his successes and failures, which enables the doctor to follow his development of skill in observation. In the appropriate column of this chart (see p. 67), if it is necessary to tell the patient where he should note the

RECORD OF TENSION CONTROL

PATIENT'S NAME_____

TYPE OF RELAXATION._____ OTHER TREATMENT._____ DAILY OCCUPATION._____

DATE	GENERAL CONDITION	INSTRUCTIONS	OLD MM.	NEW MM.	REPORT	RELAXATION	DIFFICULTIES	COMMENTS	ELEC. REC., B. P., BAS. MET.

The form illustrated here furnishes a convenient means of record for the physician to use in directing the patient in a series of instruction periods. The headings of the first three columns are self-explanatory. The fifth column is used to record muscle group locations to receive practice for the first time. (E.g., LHE, meaning extension of the left hand.) The fourth column is for a record of muscle groups that have been reviewed. The sixth column is to be used for the patient's reports, particularly of his success or failure to recognize the sensation of muscular contraction in each area. Success is indicated by the sign +, failure by the sign —; digits represent the number of reports given; S represents a spontaneous, unassisted report and I means that the patient was informed of the locality. (For details, see text.) The seventh column is used by the physician to record his observations of indications of relaxation. The eighth column is used for recording signs of restlessness, complaints and other difficulties. The ninth column is for general observations and conclusions of the physician. The tenth column is reserved for objective physiologic data, including electrical recordings, basal metabolism, blood pressure and respiratory rates and character.

control, the response is marked +1I. If the patient reports correctly without help, the mark is +1S.

Accordingly, −1+1S would mean success on the second independent response; −2S+1I would mean failures on two different occasions to locate the area without help but acknowledgment when the location was pointed out.

A common error is to confuse the control sensation (tension) with strain. Following this error, if the doctor points out the difference, the notation is abbreviated in the column headed Instructions by the terms "T. and S."

Instructions for Practice

Following each instruction period, the patient is told what he is to practice. It is important to warn him to perform only one tension per hour. Thus, the first hour of practice is to be devoted to bending back the left hand at the wrist. Arm 2 is not to be performed during the first hour. During the second hour of practice, the hand is to be bent forward only. This is what is meant by the instruction to practice only one tension per hour of practice periods at home. However, this one tension is to be performed three times during the first portion of the hour, at intervals of several minutes. Many patients perform the tensions continuously through the hour as if they were "relaxation exercises." Many continue each hour to practice the entire series of tensions on which they have previously received instructions unless the doctor discovers the error and corrects it orally.

Clarifying the Principles

Instruction on the principles of self-operations control should begin in the early periods. Issues should be distinguished from tension attitudes during the first or the second period. Other principles should be clarified as soon as possible. During the course, the doctor should return to each one of the fundamental principles. He should test the understanding of the pupil. There should develop with the course a progressively better insight. If the instructor mistakenly feels that it is sufficient for him to discuss each principle only once, he will fail to realize the rate of progressive understanding of the pupil as he acquires skill to relax. Be repeatedly discussing principles, even though they have been previously covered, he should stimulate new and useful points of view. He will find his pupil responding in terms of applications made by him in his daily life, with resultant benefits.

Often, the second period is begun by requesting the patient to approach the electric light switch and to turn it on. "The light control which we call the switch performed work," states the doctor. "Work is force times distance. The switch moved a fraction of an inch. Or, your finger performed the work. Thereupon, the light went on.

"Likewise, bending back your left hand is work. It is force times distance. The control differs from the switch, for you continue to work as long as you keep bending back your hand. The controls continue to require force to keep them in operation. But once the switch is moved to the "on" position, it remains fixed in place with no further work performance, while the light power continues on.

"There is a second point of difference. When the light in this room goes on, the lights in the same circuit in the hall become a little dimmer. But, when the power in your extensor muscles goes on, the tension tends to spread, as you may notice. (In 1884, Pflueger informed physiologists of spread of tension in frogs.)

"Now, will you please turn the switch off? Again, this is work performance by the switch and your finger. But if you are bending your hand back, thus working continuously, no work performance is required to go off with the power. All you need to accomplish is to cease working, namely, to go negative.

"Some people act as if work were needed to relax muscles. This cannot be called an illusion because they really do not have any idea of what they are doing; but it is related to an illusion because they act on a wrong principle.

"When the switch is moved to the off position, the light goes out. Therewith, the other lights on the same circuit become a little brighter. This is contrary to what occurs when your controls in one muscle group cease to operate. The resultant tendency, if any, is for other adjacent muscle groups to relax somewhat.

"Thus, due to bodily spread (a space function) and due to habit (a time function), relaxation breeds relaxation. But tension breeds tension!"

During the same period the doctor continues as follows:

"You have seen that you have no switch to turn off muscular

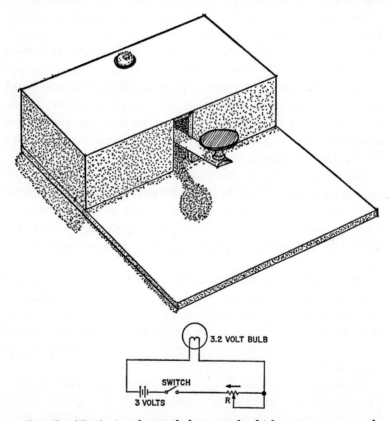

FIG. 5. (*Top*) An electric light control which operates on much the same principle as muscle control. See text. (*Bottom*) Circuit diagram. Depressing the lever progressively decreases resistance and the light grows brighter. Only when work performance lessens does the light die out.

power. Therefore, be careful in your speech. Do not say: I turned off the energy, but only, I discontinued. The control devices illustrated by the electric light switch require energy to turn them on and off; but, as you have seen, your muscular energies are subject to another type of control. I shall show you that man also devises and uses controls on this other order.

"Please sit here next to this device which we have constructed for teaching purposes. Press the key down slightly but steadily. [The room has been darkened.] As you do so, the little light bulb glows feebly. If you now press down harder, attempting to put out the light by effort, it glows all the brighter. The only way to put the light out is to discontinue your effort. This control evidently works on the same principle as that governing your muscle tension.

"Man often uses this type of control for hand manipulating. For example, when you press the ice-water button in hotels, the water flows from the faucet, but ceases when your pressure discontinues.

"To return to the device with the little light bulb, you may wonder why (if things are really so simple) people do not learn at once to relax? The device can help us to understand by analogy. Let us say that the room is dark and that you need to find something in it which requires a little light. You press the key to secure the light necessary for your purposes and, therefore, are reluctant to cease pressing.

"So it is in life. You are accustomed all day long to perform tensions to accomplish your purposes. To relax is to give up the tension together with what it seems to begin to accomplish. This, you do not wish to sacrifice and have no habit of doing so. Accordingly, as you learn to relax, your purposes become mixed. You may try to ride the horse in two different directions; to have your cake and eat it. To learn to relax requires discipline."

When the doctor has illustrated control devices, he records it in the column headed Instructions on the relaxation sheet as Control devices. (See Chart, p. 67.)

Another instruction of prime importance is to be given during one of the periods devoted to control of the arms. With the patient lying or sitting, this can be done as follows:

"Please bend your hand back once more. As we have observed and agreed, you have to work to do this and to keep it up. All tension is work. Excessive tension is unnecessary work. Then why work so much?

"Let us put the matter another way. Discontinue bending back your hand. This requires no effort. It is easy! When we say that it is hard to do anything, we mean as a rule that it requires work. If we say it is easy, we mean that it requires little or no work. Let us agree to use the word easy in this customary sense. Then we can say that to relax tension is the easiest thing in the world, for it requires just no work at all!

"If so, why does not the nervous person do this easy thing? The answer is clear. The nervous person does things the hard way! He piles up his own nervous difficulties. The tense person has developed the habit of being tense. From habit, he fails to relax.

"If you are a nervous or tense person, it is time now for you to face the facts. It is easy to relax. You may be solving problems all day long and may be loath to give this up. Having realized this clearly (step 1), find the tensions (step 2) and go negative (step 3).

"At this early stage of your training, you are to look for tensions only in the parts which we have covered. But, when you tensely solve your problems, when you are nervous, anxious or disturbed, see what you are doing in your arms! Look for the tensions there! See what you are trying to do with your arms. Then proceed to go negative!"

The order and the manner of tension instruction on the arms is given on pages 83-85. Thereafter, the doctor follows the order and the manner on the legs shown on pages 86-88. For the trunk he follows the order shown on pages 89-91.

Special instructions are included when teaching the patient chest control:

"Breathing occurs in four stages," the doctor tells him.

"First, there is the intake. Second, you may hold your breath briefly. Third, you let it out. Fourth, you pause before breathing in again.

"Take a slightly deeper breath than usual in order to give yourself a better chance to observe what happens in you. Where was the tension and when?"

The patient often indicates the sternal region, which is correct but only in part. Most often he replies that he felt tension in the place where he has indicated on holding the breath.

To improve his observation, repeated opportunities should be given without correcting him overtly. Of course, he may be led to suspect that he has been wrong or at least has not been quite correct, but, so long as his error is not indicated explicitly, he feels inclined to try again to find out for himself. This is always to be encouraged.

Emphasis should be laid on the fact that the drill tensions are selected in order to enable the *doctor* to know in advance where the tension will be felt. It would be no advantage for the *patient* to memorize these locations. On the contrary, knowing the answers in advance would prevent the doctor from testing the patient's skill in observation.

Furthermore, such rote learning would not help the patient to recognize when and where he is tense when his needs are greatest, namely, when he is engaged in his daily affairs. For then the tensions come and go in split seconds in different parts of the body not to be anticipated or delineated in advance.

"What is required for differential relaxation in daily affairs is familiarity with tensions which may occur in unpredictable regions of the body. You must be able to observe and relax fast. You must also be able to relax a part progressively when you note that tension is beginning to mount. All this calls for something quite different from memorizing where tensions are felt when you bend a toe upward or take a deep breath. Likewise, it will not help you if you form a habit of reflecting where the tension should be to pull your toe upward or to engage in some other specific act. In the daily practice of differential relaxation, there is no time for reflection. Things move too fast!"

Emphasizing Aim

After the patient has grasped the principle of self-direction by muscular controls, it is timely to emphasize to him the underlying aim, which is a new and better way of living. But this calls for clarification.

Exactly what are we trying to accomplish in this direction? We may return to comparison with driving an automobile. Let us imagine that in some future time we get into a car to go to New York. Let us imagine that the cars have been so greatly improved that we will have no need to drive by manipulating the controls as we pass over the roads. Instead, all we need to do is to set a dial to indicate our goal. We set the dial for New York and—lo and behold—without knowing how, we arrive there in due course.

We could call this "goal" riding. Such an achievement would require great ingenuity on the part of automobile engineers and manufacturers. It is doubtful that man will ever be able to create so remarkable an instrument. But nature has done so in man.

All day long man sets himself goals, interwoven in the most complex patterns. Much of his living consists in carrying them out. Other higher animals do much the same, but are much simpler in their patterns.

The physician should give examples of goals, from the simplest in character (such as a clean face or a full stomach), to the most complex (such as gaining a college degree or having a family).

Like the automobile in our fancy, which arrives without being driven, man pursues and commonly reaches his goals without knowing how and without operating his controls. As was pointed out in earlier pages, without training, he does not even know that the use of controls is available. He has achieved what we shall call goal living, thanks to the ingenuity of nature, but he has never learned to drive.

Shall we hope and expect self-operations control, the new way to live, to supplant the older way entirely? This would be impossible. Obviously, it would be undesirable. Man should always retain his goals for survival, the betterment of his lot and—doubtless, above all—spiritual gain. We teach him to drive in order to improve his selection among goals and his chances of obtaining what he selects. We teach him to count the costs in muscular energies so that he can save himself. Our purpose is to give him a new way of living which is not to supplant the old but is to be compounded with it to the best interests of the individual and society. Thus, our aim is to help him to develop a new and higher type of integration.

Trunk and Neck

Instruction on the trunk muscles is completed in the order indicated on pages 89-91. Instructions on the neck muscles follow in the order indicated on pages 92-93.

At all stages, the doctor employs the method of diminishing tensions from time to time. In this the patient contracts a muscle group (for example, arm 1), notes the control signal and subsequently is requested to "tense about half as much" and so on at brief intervals. On each occasion he reports whether he recognizes the control signal. The series ends when the signal becomes too faint for his recognition. The patient practices at this as well as at fast and at slow progressive relaxation. During class instruction and in his home practice, the tension performed should be the minimal which permits him to identify the control sensation.

Eye Region

Instructions in the eye region are indicated in order on pages 94-95. Here, as elsewhere in the body, the patient should practice observation of slight, steady tensions as well as evanescent ones. Thus, steady closure of the lids is indicated on page 94. He should practice also the observing and the reporting of what takes place during frequent, slight winking.

The order of instruction for the eye region is indicated on page 94. The pupil is to learn to recognize the eye controls in looking in different directions as well as straight ahead. (See pp. 94-95, Eye 5-7; p. 95, Eye 8-11.) Thereafter, a pen is moved from side to side at a constant rate like a clock pendulum and the patient is requested to report on what he observes in himself.

Not all patients understand the nature of a report on their own sensations. The method of such reporting is based on autosensory observation. In this connection the doctor should study the article mentioned in the bibliography entitled, On Meaning and Understanding. In accordance with the principles and methods outlined therein, he should practice on himself both in observing and in reporting. He should become familiar with the difference between processes, such as sensations, and the meanings which come and go as events in the lives of every person.

After the pen has been moved before his eyes, as described above, the patient should report that he experienced tensions in the eyes (he may call them controls) to look one way or the other or straight forward. At first report, he may speak of strain instead of tensions. If he really means the latter, he is using the wrong term for an experience which is by mutual agreement to be called tension. Accordingly, it becomes necessary to find out precisely what he means. On looking far in any direction, he should report both tension and strain but should be able to indicate the difference. A skilled observer will report tactile sensations from the lids also.

Following successful reporting, the patient closes his lids and goes negative for several minutes. Thereupon, he is requested to continue with lids closed but to imagine that he sees the pen moving to and fro at about the same rate as previously. As a rule, the doctor can note rhythmic movements of the eyeballs under the closed lids.

When the patient is requested to report what took place during imagination, he often states at once that he had much the same order of experiences as with the eyes open. He may mention tensions in the eyeballs or behind the eyeballs. This report is noted as +1S.

After another interval for eye rest, he is requested to make the pen go to and fro very slowly in imagination. This time the doctor says, "No report is necessary this time. Please say whether you made the imagined pen go more slowly: answer only yes or no."

The answer should be "yes." After another interval for eye relaxation, he is requested to make the pen go quickly to and fro in imagination. As in the previous instance, the physician asks whether he did so and requests him merely to answer yes or no.

After an affirmative answer, he is requested to make the imagined pen stand still. After he has stated that he did so, the doctor is ready to ask the crucial question as follows:

"According to your statements, you made the pen go slow in imagination, then fast and finally you made it stand still. In all this you followed my requests. How did you do this? How were you able to determine the rate at which the pen moved in your imagination?"

Wrong answers are "by my mind," "by my imagination" and "by my brain." To such wrong answers, the doctor may reply that the patient is conveying no information. Of course, when he imagined, he used his imagination, his mind or his brain. But he has not replied to the question asked. The question should be repeated.

Many patients will reply at once, "I used my eye-controls." They are told that this is right.

Following this, instruction passes to the simplest types of imagining of an object without emotional connotation, such as; a bird moves or is stationary. These types are called matters imagined in class 1 and are illustrated in the instructions under the heading Visualization, on p. 96.

Matters imagined in class 2 are those familiar in the everyday life of the individual, such as his breakfast, his living-room and the street on which he lives. Many patients, after reporting successfully on class 1, omit the report of tensions (or of eye-controls) after imagination of matters of class 2. Evidently they become engrossed in the familiar object, and, falling into old habits, fail to observe the process of tension.

After positive reports have been made on acts of imagination of familiar objects wthout emotional connotation, the doctor proceeds to request the learner to imagine matters of class 3. These are matters which concern him greatly or are associated with emotion. Such questions cannot be asked by the physician unless he knows the patient's personal history.

After sufficient practice at reporting on visual imagination, the patient is requested to go negative in the eye region. Care is taken to avoid the instruction "do not imagine" or "do not bother to imagine." After leaving him alone for 15 minutes or more, the instructor returns to ask, "Were your eyes at zero during any time?"

A negative answer is accepted at face value and another opportunity is given following the instruction, "This time, see if you can get down to zero." A positive answer is followed by the question, "For how long would you guess or estimate that your eyes were at zero tension or approximately there?"

Approved estimates, corresponding to experience in electrical recording of eye potentials, are of a few seconds or more.

Following such an answer, the patient is requested to describe what took place in him while his eyes were at or close to zero. The correct reply, which is to be given without leading questions is, "There were no visual images."

If the lids, the forehead and the brow present signs of such inactivity, the patient is requested to practice at home to lengthen this totally negative interval by a few seconds or more.

"What happens when you worry?" is a question which should evoke the reply, "I imagine visually." If so, it is in order to inquire, "What would occur if you were to relax?" "I would stop worrying for the time" is the common reply.

"Here is one good use for self-operations control," the doctor may add, drawing the evident moral.

He directs the patient to continue diligently to improve his eye technic.

Speech Region

The doctor's guide to order in the muscles of speech appears on pages 97-99.

The physician should test how rigidly the patient holds his lower jaw by grasping it firmly and moving it at the joint. It is amazing how much energy is spent needlessly in this region —not that it is necessarily all waste. Popular belief associates jaw tension with certain types of character—no doubt, justly. Primitive language often emphasizes tension and points boldly to its significance. "The Hebrews are a stiff-necked people" was said of them in their biblical record. The statement meant precisely that. To-day we might consider it to be figurative, but this would miss the directness of observation and meaning which, evidently, was dear to this tribe.

In any event, the patient is requested to stiffen the jaw a little more and to report on what he notices. Most individuals promptly point to the mandibular region as the seat of tension, ignoring the temples. Perhaps the temples are recognized spontaneously on the third occasion, following a few minutes allowed for going negative, when the patient again closes his jaw firmly. If so, the record would read Mandible: +1S, Temples −2+1S.

Following practice at recognition of jaw tension in closing and going negative, drill is given in opening the jaws. The patient is requested to relax his open jaws. As a rule, he will close them gradually. To show that he is not relaxing, he is requested to open his jaws once more and, then, very gradually close them by slow tension. Thereupon he generally does the same things which he did when he was requested to relax. To save time, the doctor may request him to relax with mouth open. Even then, as a rule, he gradually closes his jaws. Much drill is needed before he really learns, and the doctor must not let himself be deceived, but check frequently to see if the lower jaw can be pushed up and down freely.

When this has been accomplished, following the order indicated on page 97, the physician proceeds with the other chief muscle groups of speech, finally coming to counting to ten, performed aloud, repeatedly, with diminishing loudness and tension. After each counting, the patient reports and should list all speech parts. It is useful for him to develop a habit of looking for tension in each part, and to omit none. If he misses important parts in reporting what he observes during counting aloud, obviously he will miss all the more when requested to "count so slightly that I cannot even see or hear it." (On the record, this is called imperceptible.) Likewise, he will overlook tensions present during imagined counting.

After positive reports have been given concerning imagined counting, the patient is to say simple things in imagination. For example, he is to imagine saying his name and address three times; the name of the President of the United States; and the name of the city and the state in which he lives. Following such examples, he imagines saying something about matters more intimate and of greater emotional content.

It is noted whether or not he reports visual images of the matters mentioned. Most individuals overlook this or say, "I did not know that you wanted me to report on that." It is a convenient excuse for failure to note the familiar tension. The doctor should emphasize that, even at this stage of training, the patient tends to ignore important tension states and that he should be on the alert for such omissions.

"Speech," the doctor may add, "is a means of communication both external and internal to the organism. For example, it serves for giving orders in military drills. Likewise, the individual often gives internal orders by inner speech."

Combined Controls

After the patient has made it a custom to observe both ocular and speech controls, he is requested to think of or reflect on various matters of impersonal character and, later, those which concern him. He is instructed also to go negative in the eye and the speech regions and, later, to report whether he reached the zero level and for what estimated duration.

If he mentions an interval, he is requested to report on what happened or what did not happen during this interval. It is important for him to reply (without goading) that during the interval he was not thinking at all, there were no visual pictures and no inner speech, his "mind was a blank."

He is left with the instruction to practice repeatedly at this at home, going negative for increasing intervals of time in the regions of the eyes and speech.

Differential Control

Differential Control is equivalent to *Differential Relaxation* when teaching is by the parent method. Either expression stands for economy in the expenditure of muscular energies. Waste is avoided by training the individual to spare those tensions not needed for any act. For this he must become skilled in differentiating between those tensions necessary for an act, called *primary tensions,* and those which are unnecessary and, therefore, are called *secondary.* Obviously, before he can become discriminating, he must learn to recognize tensions and control the on and off phases of muscular power. These matters should be discussed.

In the sitting posture, the order of performance is sufficiently indicated on pages 100 to 115. The doctor should elicit the slightest tension in any practice which leads to recognition. If the subject is sufficiently skillful, the movement, if any, should be less than grossly visible. Often it will suffice to have him engage merely in imagination.

He should be encouraged to observe what he does during the conduct of his daily affairs. When events of importance arise, he may give his attention to them exclusively. To some extent, at least, he will depend for differential control on the habits which he has formed previously. However, when routine matters are performed, such as opening the morning's mail, he should look for undue tensions and proceed to diminish or eliminate them. By repetition during daily activities, the individual conditions himself to the employment of control in similar circumstances.

As the doctor will find, the new way of living has not yet taken hold. He should review the principles of scientific relaxation and of self-operations control for each patient. In this way, new insight will be gained.

Practices involving imagination, reflection and emotion must be given afresh when the regions of the eyes and speech are covered in the sitting posture. The instructor should find his pupil increasingly observant and adept at going negative.

At all points of the training the doctor will be aided if graphs of the patient's tension states are available to him. These graphs will be plots of action-potentials against time from tests before and during the earlier portion of training made while the patient is lying and others made with the patient in the sitting posture before and during the teaching of differential control. In the graphs the doctor will see indications of where the patient is doing well and where he is not. To the knowledge of how his pupil is progressing gained from the pupil's accounts and from his own gross observation, the doctor can add that gained from the graphs. Thus he can judge better and help more.

However useful, methods of measurement are not indispensible in clinical practice. Many clinicians get along without them, relying on their clinical observations and the other methods outlined in this and the following chapter.

CHAPTER **6**

Practice Schedule
With Instructions
and Illustrations

NOTE: The contents of this chapter together with appropriate introductory material are published as a separate booklet with the title *Self-Operations Control*. It is especially designed for distribution to patients as a guide for home practice sessions. A copy of the pamphlet will be found at the back of the book. Additional copies may be obtained from J. B. Lippincott Co., Philadelphia 5, Pa.

ARM PRACTICE

In each daily practice period, follow the appropriate photograph, performing the tension indicated 3 times at intervals of several minutes. These are *NOT* exercises. Interest yourself in becoming familiar with the control sensation in each part so that you can learn really to run yourself properly relaxed under all conditions.

DAY	LEFT ARM	DAY	RIGHT ARM
1.	Bend hand back.	8.	Bend hand back.
2.	Bend hand forward.	9.	Bend hand forward.
3.	Relax only.	10.	Relax only.
4.	Bend at elbow.	11.	Bend at elbow.
5.	Press wrist down on books.	12.	Press wrist down on books.
6.	Relax only.	13.	Relax only.
7.	Progressive tension and relaxation of whole arm.	14.	Progressive tension and relaxation of whole arm.

Arm 1   Lying

PERIOD No. 1

Select a quiet room, free from intruders and phone calls.

1. Lying on your back with arms at sides, leave eyes open 3 to 4 minutes.

2. Gradually close eyes and keep them closed entire hour.

3. After 3 to 4 minutes with eyes closed, bend left hand back (see illustration), observing the control sensation 1 to 2 minutes and how it differs from the strains in the wrist and in the lower portion of the forearm.

4. Go negative for 3 to 4 minutes.

5. Again bend left hand back and observe as previously.

6. Once more go negative 3 to 4 minutes.

7. Bend left hand back a third and last time, observing the control sensation 1 to 2 minutes.

8. Finally go negative for remainder of hour.

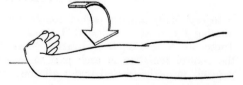

Arm 1: Lying
Bend hand back. (Felt in back upper part of forearm)

Arm 2: Lying
Bend hand forward. (Felt in front of forearm)

Arm 3   Lying

PERIOD NO. 3

Lie quietly on back as previously, arms at sides. In this and in all subsequent periods lying down, leave eyes open several minutes, then gradually close them and keep closed for entire hour. Throughout this period go negative only: Do not bend, extend or stiffen the arm; but if you should do so, awaredly or unawaredly, note the slight control sensation which will thereupon appear in the left arm and go negative there at once.

Do not tense to relax.

In General

Period No. 3 is called a *zero* period.

Hereafter, every third period is to be a zero period. In the other practice periods, specialize on one tension only, performing this three times.

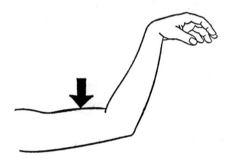

Arm 4: Lying
Bend arm at elbow, about 35°. (Felt in biceps, front of upper arm)

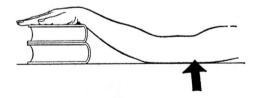

Arm 5: Lying
Press wrist down against books. (Felt in back part of upper arm)

LEG PRACTICE
Lying

In each daily practice period, follow the appropriate photograph, performing the tension indicated 3 times at intervals of several minutes. These are *NOT* exercises. Interest yourself in becoming familiar with the control sensation in each part so that you can learn really to run yourself properly relaxed under all conditions.

DAY	LEFT LEG	DAY	RIGHT LEG
1.	Bend foot up.	11.	Bend foot up.
2.	Bend foot down.	12.	Bend foot down.
3.	Relax only.	13.	Relax only.
4.	Raise foot.	14.	Raise foot.
5.	Bend at knee.	15.	Bend at knee.
6.	Relax only.	16.	Relax only.
7.	Raise knee.	17.	Raise knee.
8.	Press lower thigh down.	18.	Press lower thigh down.
9.	Relax entire left leg.	19.	Relax entire right knee.
10.	Progressive tension and relaxation of entire left leg	20.	Progressive tension and relaxation of entire right leg.

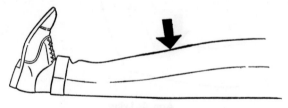

Leg 1: Lying
Bend foot up. (Felt along front of lower leg)

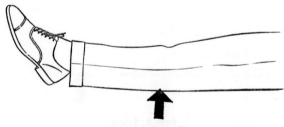

Leg 2: Lying
Extend foot. (Felt in calf)

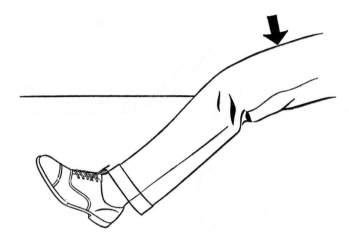

Leg 4: Lying
Raise foot and leg. (Felt in front part of thigh)

Leg 5: Lying
Bend leg at knee. (Felt along back of thigh)

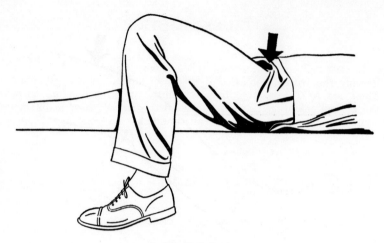

Leg 7: Lying
Raise knee, bending at hip. (Felt in muscles deep in abdomen, toward back, near hip)

Leg 8: Lying
Press lower thigh against books. (Felt in buttocks)

TRUNK PRACTICE
Lying

In each daily practice period, follow the appropriate photograph, performing the tension indicated 3 times at intervals of several minutes. These are *NOT* exercises. Interest yourself in becoming familiar with the control sensation in each part so that you can learn really to run yourself properly relaxed under all conditions.

DAY TRUNK
1. Pull in abdomen.
2. Arch back slightly.
3. Relax abdomen, back and legs.
4. Observe during a deeper breath.
5. Bend shoulders back.
6. Relax only.
7. Left arm forward and inward.
8. Right arm forward and inward.
9. Relax only.
10. Elevate shoulders.

Trunk 1: Lying
Pull in abdomen. (Felt faintly all over abdomen)

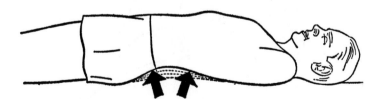

Trunk 2: Lying
Arch the back. (Felt definitely along both sides of the spine)

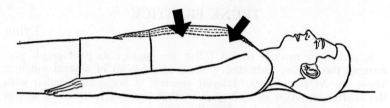

Trunk 4: Lying
Observe during a deeper breath. (Very
faint diffuse tenseness felt all over chest)

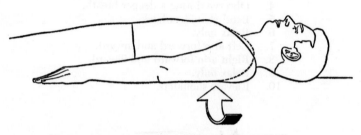

Trunk 5: Lying
Bend shoulders back. (Felt in back,
between shoulder blades)

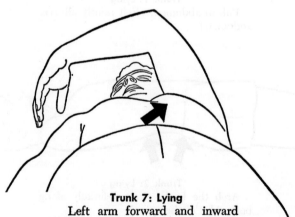

Trunk 7: Lying
Left arm forward and inward
(Felt in front of chest near left
arm)

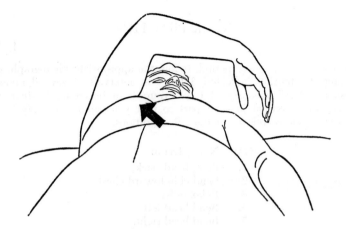

Trunk 8: Lying
Right arm forward and inward (Felt
in front of chest on right)

Trunk 10: Lying
Elevate shoulders. (Felt along top of
shoulders and in sides of neck)

NECK PRACTICE

Lying

In each daily practice period, follow the appropriate photograph, performing the tension indicated 3 times at intervals of several minutes. These are *NOT* exercises. Interest yourself in becoming familiar with the control sensation in each part so that you can learn really to run yourself properly relaxed under all conditions.

Day	Neck, Lying
1.	Bend head back.
2.	Bend chin toward chest.
3.	Relax only.
4.	Bend head left.
5.	Bend head right.
6.	Relax only.

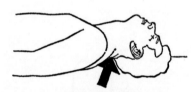

Neck 1: Lying
Bend head back. (Felt in back of neck, perhaps below, in back)

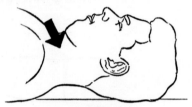

Neck 2: Lying
Bend chin down. (Felt in sides of neck)

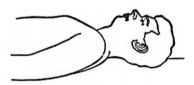

Neck 3: Lying
Relax only.

Neck 4: Lying
Bend head left. (Felt in left side of neck)

Neck 5: Lying
Bend head right. (Felt
in right side of neck)

Neck 6: Lying
Relax only.

EYE REGION PRACTICE
Lying

In each daily practice period, follow the appropriate photograph, performing the tension indicated 3 times at intervals of several minutes. These are *NOT* exercises. Interest yourself in becoming familiar with the control sensation in each part so that you can learn really to run yourself properly relaxed under all conditions.

DAY	EYE REGION
1.	Wrinkle forehead.
2.	Frown.
3.	Relax only.
4.	Close eyelids tightly.
5.	Look left with lids closed.
6.	Relax only.
7.	Look right with lids closed.
8.	Look up.
9.	Relax only.
10.	Look downward with lids closed.
11.	Look forward with lids closed.
12.	Relax only.

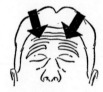

Eye Region 1: Lying
Wrinkle forehead.
(Felt diffusely over entire forehead)

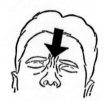

Eye Region 2: Lying
Frown. (Felt distinctly between eyes)

Eye Region 4: Lying
Close eyelids tightly. (Felt all over eyelids)

Eye Region 5: Lying
Look up (eyelids closed.) (Felt in eyeball muscles at top; tensions change rapidly as eyes move.)

Eye Region 7: Lying
Look right (eye-
lids closed). (Felt
in eyeball muscles,
right; note static and
moving tensions.)

Eye Region 8: Lying
Look left (eyelids
closed.) (Felt in eye-
ball muscles, left)

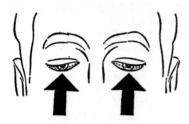

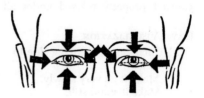

Eye Region 11: Lying
Look forward
(eyelids closed). (Felt
in muscles all
around eyeballs)

Eye Region 10: Lying
Look down (eye-
lids closed.) (Felt in
eyeball muscles, be-
low)

VISUALIZATION PRACTICE

Lying

with lids open
with lids closed

In each daily practice period, follow the appropriate photograph, performing the tension indicated 3 times at intervals of several minutes. These are *NOT* exercises. Interest yourself in becoming familiar with the control sensation in each part so that you can learn really to run yourself properly relaxed under all conditions.

DAY	VISUALIZATION	DAY	VISUALIZATION
1.	Imagine pen moving side to side.	4.	Bird flying from tree to tree. Bird still.
	Make it go very slowly.	5.	Ball rolling on ground.
	Make it stand still.		Ball still.
	Make it go very fast.		Eiffel tower.
2.	Skyrocket.	6.	Relax only.
	Train passing quickly.	7.	Rabbit on road.
	Man walking by.		Head of pin.
3.	Relax eyes to zero.	8.	President of U. S.
		9.	Relax only.

SPEECH REGION PRACTICE
Lying

In each daily practice period, follow the appropriate photograph, performing the tension indicated 3 times at intervals of several minutes. These are *NOT* exercises. Interest yourself in becoming familiar with the control sensation in each part so that you can learn really to run yourself properly relaxed under all conditions.

DAY
1. Close jaws somewhat firmly.
2. Open jaws.
3. Relax only.
4. Show teeth (as if smiling).
5. Pout.
6. Relax only.
7. Push tongue forward against teeth.
8. Pull tongue backward.
9. Relax only.
10. Count to 10.
11. Count half as loudly.
12. Relax only.

DAY
13. Count very faintly.
14. Count imperceptibly.
15. Relax only.
16. Imagine that you are counting.
17. Imagine you are saying alphabet.
18. Relax only.
19. Imagine saying name three times.
Address three times.
Name of President three times.

Speech Region 1: Lying
Close jaws rather firmly. (Felt at back of lower jaw and in temples)

Speech Region 2: Lying
Open jaws. (Felt in sides of lower jaw and neck)

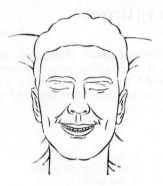

Speech Region 4: Lying
Show teeth (as if
smiling). (Felt in
cheeks)

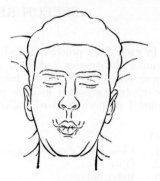

Speech Region 5: Lying
Pout. (Felt in and
around lips)

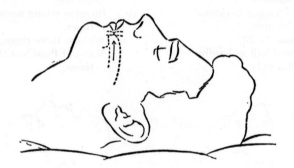

Speech Region 7: Lying
Push tongue against teeth. (Felt in
tongue)

Speech Region 8: Lying
Pull tongue backward. (Felt in tongue and floor of mouth)

Speech Region 10: Lying
Count to 10. (Felt in cheeks, lips, tongue, jaw muscles, muscles, throat, chest and, perhaps, abdomen)

ARM PRACTICE
Sitting

In each daily practice period, follow the appropriate photograph, performing the tension indicated 3 times at intervals of several minutes. These are *NOT* exercises. Interest yourself in becoming familiar with the control sensation in each part so that you can learn really to run yourself properly relaxed under all conditions.

Day	Left Arm	Day	Right Arm
1.	Bend hand back.	8.	Bend hand back.
2.	Bend hand forward.	9.	Bend hand forward.
3.	Relax only.	10.	Relax only.
4.	Bend at elbow.	11.	Bend at elbow.
5.	Press wrist down.	12.	Press wrist down.
6.	Relax only.	13.	Relax only.
7.	Progressive tension and relaxation of whole arm.	14.	Progressive tension and relaxation of whole arm.

Arm 1: Sitting
Bend hand back. (Felt in back part of forearm)

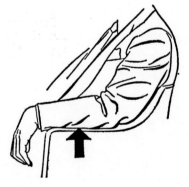

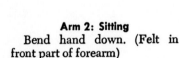

Arm 2: Sitting
Bend hand down. (Felt in front part of forearm)

Arm 4: Sitting
Bend arm at elbow. (Felt in
biceps, front of upper arm)

Arm 5: Sitting
Press wrist down against
arm of chair. (Felt in back,
upper arm)

LEG PRACTICE
Sitting

In each daily practice period, follow the appropriate photograph, performing the tension indicated 3 times at intervals of several minutes. These are *NOT* exercises. Interest yourself in becoming familiar with the control sensation in each part so that you can learn really to run yourself properly relaxed under all conditions.

DAY	LEFT LEG	DAY	RIGHT LEG
1.	Bend foot up.	11.	Bend foot up.
2.	Press down toe end of foot.	12.	Press down toe end of foot.
3.	Relax only.	13.	Relax only.
4.	Raise left foot (without moving thigh)	14.	Raise right foot (without moving thigh)
5.	Pull heel back (without moving thigh)	15.	Pull heel back (without moving thigh)
6.	Relax only.	16.	Relax only.
7.	Press down whole foot.	17.	Press down whole foot.
8.	Raise knee while foot hangs limply.	18.	Raise knee while foot hangs limply.
9.	Relax entire left leg.	19.	Relax entire right leg.
10.	Progressive tension and relaxation of entire left leg.	20.	Progressive tension and relaxation of entire right leg.

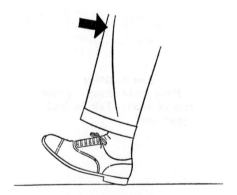

Leg 1: Sitting
Bend foot up. (Felt along front of lower leg)

Leg 2: Sitting
Press toe end of foot
down. (Felt in calf)

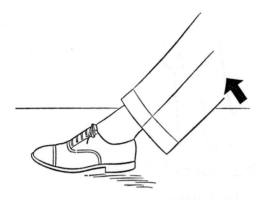

Leg 4: Sitting
Raise foot without moving
thigh. (Felt in front of thigh)

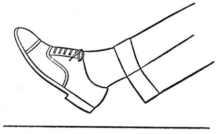

Leg 5: Sitting
Pull heel back
without moving
thigh. (Felt along
back of thigh)

Leg 7: Sitting
Press down whole
foot. (Felt in buttocks)

Leg 8: Sitting
Raise knee while foot
hangs limply. (Felt in
psoas muscles, deep in abdomen, toward back)

TRUNK PRACTICE
Sitting

In each daily practice period, follow the appropriate photograph, performing the tension indicated 3 times at intervals of several minutes. These are *NOT* exercises. Interest yourself in becoming familiar with the control sensation in each part so that you can learn really to run yourself properly relaxed under all conditions.

DAY TRUNK
1. Pull in abdomen.
2. Arch back slightly.
3. Relax abdomen, back and legs.
4. Observe during a deeper breath.
5. Bend shoulders back.
6. Relax only.
7. Left arm forward and inward.
8. Right arm forward and inward.
9. Relax only.
10. Elevate shoulder.

Trunk 1: Sitting
Pull in abdomen.
(Felt faintly all over abdomen)

Trunk 2: Sitting
Sit up straight. (Felt definitely along both sides of spine)

Trunk 4: Sitting
Observe during a
deeper breath. (Very
faint diffuse tenseness
felt all over chest)

Trunk 5: Sitting
Pull shoulders back.
(Felt in back between
shoulder blades)

Trunk 6: Sitting
Relax only.

Trunk 7: Sitting
Left arm forward and
inward. (Felt in front of
chest on left)

Trunk 8: Sitting
Right arm forward
and inward. (Felt in
front of chest on right)

Trunk 9: Sitting
Relax only.

Trunk 10: Sitting
Elevate shoulders.
(Felt along top of shoul-
ders and in sides of
neck)

NECK PRACTICE
Sitting

In each daily practice period, follow the appropriate photograph, performing the tension indicated 3 times at intervals of several minutes. These are *NOT* exercises. Interest yourself in becoming familiar with the control sensation in each part so that you can learn really to run yourself properly relaxed under all conditions.

DAY   NECK, SITTING
1. Bend head back slightly.
2. Bend chin toward chest.
3. Relax only.
4. Bend head right.
5. Bend head left.
6. Relax only.
7. Head erect. Relax neck as far as possible.

Neck 1: Sitting
Bend head back slightly. (Felt in back of neck and, perhaps, below in back)

Neck 2: Sitting
Bend chin down. (Felt in sides of neck)

Neck 3: Sitting
Relax only.

Neck 4: Sitting
Bend head right.
(Felt in right side of
neck)

Neck 5: Sitting
Bend head left. (Felt
in left side of neck)

EYE REGION PRACTICE

Sitting

In each daily practice period, follow the appropriate photograph, performing the tension indicated 3 times at intervals of several minutes. These are *NOT* exercises. Interest yourself in becoming familiar with the control sensation in each part so that you can learn really to run yourself properly relaxed under all conditions.

DAY	EYE REGION
1.	Wrinkle forehead.
2.	Frown.
3.	Relax only.
4.	Close eyelids tightly.
5.	Look left with lids closed.
6.	Relax only.
7.	Look right with lids closed.
8.	Look up.
9.	Relax only.
10.	Look downward with lids closed.
11.	Look forward with lids closed.
12.	Relax only.

Eye Region 1: Sitting
Wrinkle forehead.
(Felt diffusely all over forehead)

Eye Region 2: Sitting
Frown. (Felt distinctly between eyes)

Eye Region 5: Sitting
Look left. (Felt in eyeball muscles on left)

Eye Region 7: Sitting
Look right. (Felt in eyeball muscles on right)

Eye Region 4: Sitting
Close eyes tightly. (Felt all over eyelids)

Eye Region 8: Sitting
Look up. (Felt in eyeball muscles above)

Eye Region 10: Sitting
Look down. (Felt in eyeball muscles below)

Eye Region II: Sitting
Look forward. (Felt in eyeball muscles all all around the eyes)

VISUALIZATION PRACTICE

Sitting

with lids open
with lids closed

In each daily practice period, follow the appropriate photograph, performing the tension indicated 3 times at intervals of several minutes. These are *NOT* exercises. Interest yourself in becoming familiar with the control sensation in each part so that you can learn really to run yourself properly relaxed under all conditions.

DAY	VISUALIZATION	DAY	VISUALIZATION
1.	Imagine pen moving side to side.	4.	Bird flying from tree to tree.
	Make it go very slowly.		Bird still.
	Make it stand still.	5.	Ball rolling on ground.
	Make it go very fast.		Ball still.
2.	Skyrocket.		Eiffel tower.
	Train passing quickly.	6.	Relax only.
	Man walking by.	7.	Rabbit on road.
3.	Relax eyes to zero.		Head of pin.
		8.	President of U. S.
		9.	Relax only.

SPEECH REGION PRACTICE
Sitting

In each daily practice period, follow the appropriate photograph, performing the tension indicated 3 times at intervals of several minutes. These are *NOT* exercises. Interest yourself in becoming familiar with the control sensation in each part so that you can learn really to run yourself properly relaxed under all conditions.

DAY

1. Close jaws somewhat firmly.
2. Open jaws.
3. Relax only.
4. Show teeth (as if smiling).
5. Pout.
6. Relax only.
7. Push tongue forward against teeth.
8. Pull tongue backward.
9. Relax only.
10. Count to 10.
11. Count half as loud.
12. Relax only.

DAY

13. Count very faintly.
14. Count imperceptibly.
15. Relax only.
16. Imagine that you are counting.
17. Imagine you are saying alphabet.
18. Relax only.
19. Imagine saying name three times.
    Address three times.
    Name of President three times.

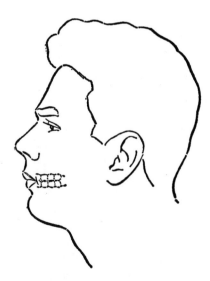

Speech Region 1: Sitting
Close jaws somewhat firmly. (Felt at back of lower jaw and in temple)

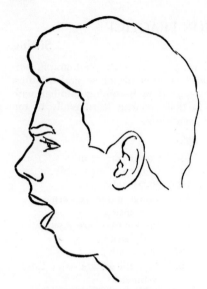

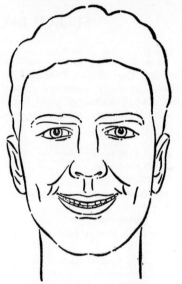

Speech Region 2: Sitting
Open jaws. (Felt in sides of
lower jaw and neck)

Speech Region 4: Sitting
Show teeth, as if smiling.
(Felt in cheeks)

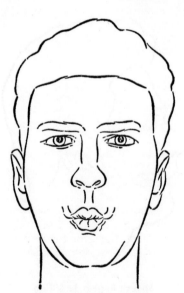

Speech Region 5: Sitting
Pout. (Felt in and around
lips)

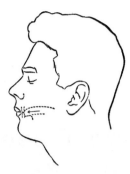 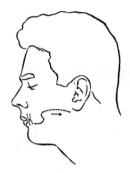

Speech Region 7: Sitting
Push tongue forward against teeth. (Felt in tongue)

Speech Region 8: Sitting
Pull tongue backward. (Felt in tongue and floor of mouth)

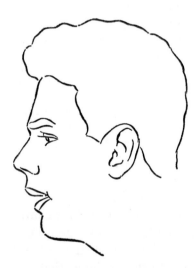

Speech Region 10: Sitting
Count to 10. (Felt in cheeks, lips, tongue, jaw, throat, chest and, perhaps, abdomen.

CHAPTER 7

Illustrative Cases

Tension disorders are manifested in symptoms and signs in every system of the organism, with endless individual differences and temporal changes. It is impossible to illustrate their variety fully or adequately in the present chapter. A small number of case histories, indicating the present-day approach, will be presented briefly.

In self-operations control, the patient receives instruction enabling him to observe what he is really doing at the moment of effort-tension in order to learn some measure of effective control. He is to be taught to do better for himself, so far as neuromuscular tension is concerned, than drugs can do for him. This is an educational process.

I shall illustrate that self-operations control carefully avoids therapeutic suggestion and autosuggestion. In teaching a person to become an airplane pilot, the instructor would only do harm by suggesting to the beginner that he is becoming good or that he need not worry, or by leading him to talk to himself autosuggestively. On the contrary, the good teacher does not minimize objective difficulties to be encountered in ascending or landing or in unfavorable weather conditions while flying. What is needed in a pilot is skill in meeting unfavorable conditions with only that degree of self-confidence which is fitting. Similarly, as the following case histories will bring out, the aim in education of the patient is the cultivation of skill in meeting hardships and difficulties rather than the nurturing of self-confidence or belief in good results through any form of suggestion. The following *greatly condensed* case histories will illustrate what a wide range of medical conditions can be met successfully by tension control. Accounts of action-potential measurements are omitted.

CASE 1. TENSION, COLITIS, SWEATING, BARBITURATE HABITUATION

The patient was white, male, 28 years of age; born in Chicago, of Swedish descent; married; an engineer and salesman. He was first seen in February, 1956. He complained chiefly of frequent bowel movements, with abdominal discomfort that occurred when he was visiting his customers; sweating of hands and feet, and tight muscles in the back of his shoulders, which his wife often relieved by massage. He had been taking phenobarbital for these symptoms daily for 14 years, ever since their onset. He emphasized that his nervous symptoms interfered with his social activities no less than with his business. At time, he had as many as 15 bowel movements in a day.

On examination the patient appeared healthy and well developed in conformity with his age. He did not exhibit fidgets or other overt signs of marked restlessness. His pulse was 72, his blood pressure, 115/50 in the sitting position. In general, the findings were negative, other than slight infection of the pharynx, slight furring of the tongue posteriorly and slight enlargement of the prostate.

Blood examination revealed 5,470,000 red cells per ml., with 16.5 GM per cent of hemoglobin. There were 4,300 white cells, of which 57 per cent were neutrophils, 32 per cent lymphocytes and 9 per cent mononuclears. Basal metabolic tests gave values of minus 6 per cent and minus 3 per cent on two successive tests. Analyses of the urine, the sputum and the blood, including the Kahn, were negative, as were also, the electrocardiogram, roentgenologic findings, and the findings in the chest and the teeth.

Recordings of muscular action-potentials were made systematically from time to time but will not be reported here because of lack of space and because they failed to give as much useful information in this case as in most others.

Barbiturate Habit Broken

Instruction in self-operations control was begun on February 22, 1956, in accordance with principles outlined in foregoing chapters. As an engineer, the patient was greatly interested in learning self-engineering. He stated his impression that much of what he was told "falls under the category of feedback" and he wrote a paper on this.

Following the sixth hour period of instruction, he spontaneously cut down his daily dosage of phenobarbital tablets from 4 to 2. Not long after this, he discontinued the sedative altogether and did not resume its use.

However, during the early months of instruction there were times when symptoms returned severely, including fatigue in the legs. Nevertheless, by April 20th he was able to report, "I believe that I can handle myself better now than when I began." On that date abdominal cramping pain set in during the period of instruction. After 15 minutes of muscle inactivation, he stated that the pain had disappeared completely. Interpreting this, we assume that the intestinal cramping relaxed on progressive skeletal neuromuscular relaxation.

Another of the troublesome symptoms was reported on May 18, when the patient complained that "he had not been able to relax for a week." The palms of his hands had been sweating, and there had been a "kink" in the back of his neck whenever he sat at his desk (a symptom recurrent when he became tense ever since he was struck on the back of his head by a baseball some years ago.)

He was interested again with the instructions concerning wrinkling his forehead and frowning, and he commented, "I can feel myself do this all day long!" I replied that this was quite visible to an observer.

Relapse

In mid-July a moderate relapse in symptoms set in. He ascribed this to his becoming unduly tense when he and his wife were having trouble with her family and when he was getting ready for a new job in Chicago.

On December 12, instruction in the lying posture was completed. Thereafter, for instruction he sat in an office chair.

On March 1, 1957, the return of abdominal cramping pain was reported after freedom therefrom during the previous 6 months.

Continuous and Complete Freedom From Symptoms

On July 5, 1957 he reported absence of abdominal cramps and of all the other original complaints and symptoms. He felt good and looked good. This improvement, without dependence on sedative drugs, proved to be lasting. On September 27, 1957 he was discharged. The symptoms which had been chronic since the age of 14 for 14 years, with slight transient exceptions, were no longer present. The total number of hours of instruction had been 69.

In follow-up, he returned in January, 1958, reporting that he continued to be symptom-free.

CASE 2. PYLORIC ULCER (OBSTRUCTIVE)

WITH ANXIETY TENSIONS

The patient was a prominent physician, 42 years old, white, male, married, with three children. He had complained for years of severe symptoms from what had been diagnosed as pyloric ulcer. Surgery had been recommended, but he preferred to try medical relaxation methods first. He was first seen on April 1, 1956. There was pain, severe muscle cramping, anxiety and, also, "tension headaches." Cramping pains in the epigastrium radiated to the back and often were followed by burning sensations in the anorectal region. Evacuations of spastic type ranged from one to six per day, marked by moderate flatulence and eructation. The patient complained of feeling depressed and worried with "a lot of apprehensions." During the previous 3 months he had been on an ulcer diet and medication, including Pro-Banthine. He mentioned chronic nasal obstruction and nasal drip.

Six years previously, a fibrocaseous tubercle had been identified in the right pulmonary apex. The patient's colon appeared spastic in examination, and he vomited daily before breakfast. Bed rest was prescribed for months. Nevertheless, during the following year, roentgenograms revealed a spread of the tuberculous disease. He returned to bed rest for 6 months, after which he was able to proceed with his medical courses and duties. The gastrointestinal symptoms subsided gradually, returning only when he became nervous or "upset."

During his wife's first pregnancy in 1946, the patient's duodenal bulb was found to be spastic but not ulcerous. Between 1942 and 1956, he vomited before breakfast whenever he had to undertake an unusual task. His wife also suffered from tuberculosis. In 1953, his daughter suffered an accidental injury, and his mother underwent a critical operation. Following these emotional shocks, examination of the patient disclosed pyloric ulcer and scars. He followed ulcer diet, but, in December 1955, obstruction was diagnosed at the pyloric junction.

Instruction in tension control, following procedures described in foregoing chapters, was begun on March 30, 1956. Meetings were arranged monthly in New York. At first he was a difficult pupil, in contrast with most doctors, who learn present technics readily; perhaps his early responses were held down by misgivings, depression and skepticism. Nevertheless, on May 25th, he appeared less wan—perhaps a little less ill—but, still, obviously overemotional.

Begins To Employ Technic

By November 18, 1956, the date of the 19th hour-period of instruction, his skepticism (rare in a doctor) had vanished and he reported, "I use the technic now! When I was all keyed up on a business trip, I returned home, practiced for one hour and was a new person." He had discovered for himself that nervous tension is also muscular tension and that neuromuscular relaxation is the physiologic opposite.

Lessened Anxiety

He learned to discriminate objective matters about which he became anxious from the subjective anxiety tension-image pattern. This helped to assuage his recurrent anxiety in regard to flying. When all passengers were lost in a local plane crash, he was obliged to go to the morgue to identify the remains of his cousin and her husband. Even after this experience, he still succeeded in controlling his anxiety in regard to planes to such an extent that he flew frequently.

Apparently, his recovery has been virtually complete.* He learned sufficient control to be able to attend personally both to his mother, following a stroke which left her bedridden and incontinent, and also to his father, who had become paralytic. He was obliged to supply with funds his parents in addition to meeting the needs of his own family. When he was seen in September, 1963, he had been well for years, working vigorously and acting with confidence in official capacities in various medical organizations.

CASE 3. EXTREME SWEATING, TENSION DISORDER

The patient was a civil engineer, 22 years old, single, white, born in Michigan. He was referred by Dr. E. Dulsky of the Chicago Sociological Institute on January 20, 1950. The condition for which he was referred—abnormal sweating—was one of the most severe that I have ever seen. The perspiration literally dripped from his hands. Shaking hands was an ordeal which he tried to avoid. Because of his embarrassment, he seldom went out with girls and preferred solitude to social functions. At times he became depressed over his lack of accomplishment; yet, lacking self-confidence, he feared to go ahead. He complained also of "internal nervousness," which had been diagnosed as anxiety complex by Army doctors when he had been in the service. His bowels moved irregularly. Backache at times became so severe that he could hardly stand.

Sweating had been excessive since the patient was 8 years old. His father—a minister—was a mild-mannered man. His

---

* He attributes his organic recovery to Self Operation Control.

mother was a kind but domineering woman. When he was a child, she often kept him from playing freely with other boys of the neighborhood. Even before his eighth year, he lacked self-confidence in games. His father forbade him to play football because it was too dangerous and kept him safely in sight when in the country on vacations. "As I came into the 4th grade," he related, "I had a certain anxiety that people would make fun of me in sports." There had been times in his childhood when he was so nervous that he could not eat normally for weeks. During the last years of his father's life, he could not swallow solid food (evidently esophagospasm).

Examination disclosed a healthy youth of 22 of very tense appearance with fair skin and the most severe sweating of palms, axillae, feet and crotch. His pupils were somewhat large and overreactive to light and accommodation. His blood pressure was 118/56 and his pulse 80 in the sitting position.

Clinical laboratory tests were substantially negative, including sputum, urine, blood tests (Kahn negative) electrocardiogram and roentgenograms of the chest. Basal metabolic rates near lower limits of normal, together with low blood pressure values, led me to suspect the possibility of chronic fatigue. Dental roentgenograms indicated some measure of bone recession.

Instruction in self-engineering was begun on January 29, 1951. Thereafter, as a rule, he returned once a week for an hour, practicing at home each day. Even though he missed three instruction periods in March, on April 18 there was considerably less perspiring along with reduced nervous tension.

On April 25 he reported that he had changed his job. Because he had to travel, his attendance and practice became somewhat neglected. On some days he was up at 8 A.M. and did not return to his room until 2 to 3 A.M. This change caused a recurrence of perspiration. On May 3, when he removed his shoes, he displayed socks that were completely wet.

Decrease of Perspiration

On June 13, on clasping his hand, it was found to be no longer even clammy, but almost dry. On July 2 his hands were still dry, notwithstanding another change of job and the presence of coryza. On July 18, a very hot day, there was return of excessive perspiration, but, as a rule, this had diminished greatly.

The diminution evidently affected his entire outlook and associations. Now he became able to associate with the opposite sex without embarrassment, and, on January 9, 1952 he announced that he was going to be married in June.

He was seen last on March 10, 1952, having received a total of 38 hours of instruction in about 14 months. He was not considered ready for discharge, since his course was only half completed and he still had symptoms ascribed to excessive tension in the digestive tract. However, his general improvement included the diminution of perspiration toward normality.*

CASE 4. POSTCORONARY INFARCTION

The patient was a man of 66, white, retired, married. He was first seen on April 21, 1959. He complained chiefly of aching legs, insomnia, severe fatigue, lack of interest, depression, discouragement and tension. He believed that his general resistance was lowered. He had been taking sleeping pills every night for one year with unsatisfactory results.

In October, 1956, after having substernal pain for about 3 days, he walked up 5 flights of stairs then sat down "perspiring and sick all over." He drove to a doctor's office, where a diagnosis of coronary infarction was made. After 2 months of rest at home, he returned to work limited to 4 hours per day.

General examination revealed a man of placid appearance showing concern but not fidgets; he was gray-haired and somewhat bald, 67½ inches in height and about 155 lb. in weight. The abdominal walls were slack and pudgy. Aside from signs of mild senile emphysema, there was little outstanding gross pathology.

The electrocardiogram now was within normal limits, as also, were films of the chest and the findings in the blood, the urine and the sputum. Likewise, the Kahn test was negative. Basal

---

* The reader may recall that stimulating the peripheral end of the sciatic nerve in the cat produced beads of perspiration on the paw.

metabolic rates were minus 19 per cent in two successive tests. Blood calcium was 12 Mg. per cent and total blood cholesterol was 162.5 Mg. per cent. No dental pathology was noted except root absorption and deep pocketing of one tooth.

After electrical recording, instruction in self-operations control was begun on April 23, 1959. He was informed that learning would probably proceed more slowly and require more frequent hours of instruction than it did in youth. Accordingly, at first he appeared for instruction about three times per week. In addition he practiced, following printed instructions, 2 hours per day.

On May 15, he reported improvement in sleep: "The finest night since I don't know when!"

On July 3, he added that, at first, during periods of practice, he had discomfort in the region of the diaphragm, but this was no longer so. "I can see myself coming along in many ways."

Discontinues Hypnotic Drugs.

The use of sleeping pills was discontinued voluntarily as his rest improved, but aspirin and A.P.C. were used for a time when pain in the legs continued. However, on July 29 his wife noted that he had evidently gained "in tension control as well as in mental attitude and appearance." Soon thereafter leg pains began to diminish and then disappeared for about 4 months. He attributed this to learning to relax his eye and jaw muscles. Relapse set in about December 15. When he began to try to figure out why, he was warned that relapses are common and that, in place of wasting energy conjecturing causes, he needed to learn during relapses how to handle them effectively. On a later day he added, "I often think of my legs; have them in mind." He indicated his understanding and experience that control of this kind of representative activity evidently was needed. When he was restless, he discovered tensions in his legs as if he were about to move them.

Relief of Other Symptoms

He discovered from his practice that simultaneous relaxation of the eye and the speech musculatures "relieves the mind."

On February 12, he reported that he continued to sleep soundly and that the leg pains had disappeared. Differential Control in the sitting posture was begun at about this time.

On March 18, he reported that his bowel action had become regular and free from constipation.

On May 18, 1960 he commented that he had seen no real relief until after 6 months practice of tension control. Now, however, he no longer was "up and down all night with leg pains, as when I first came for instruction," but, on the contrary, he slept well without pills and without leg distress.

At his final examination he disclosed a cheerful appearance, contrasting with his anxious expression on admittance, his voice was free of its former plaintive timbre and his musculature was apparently more relaxed, with absence of the restless movements that were present formerly.

Follow-up

After his discharge in May, 1962 he and his wife traveled over the country in a trailer. He has sent quarterly reports by mail (including April 18, 1963) that he has practiced twice a day and has had slight relapses which he has handled successfully. As a rule, he has been almost completely free from symptoms without medication and has continued to be in a generally happy state of mind.

CASE 5. EARLY ESSENTIAL HYPERTENSION PLUS ANXIETY AND INSOMNIA

The patient was a somewhat stocky white man, 54 years old, an engineer and industrialist. He was first seen on December 6, 1957. He said that he was in good health, yet he was apparently anxious about a diagnosis of essential hypertension of early type. Usually, he recounted, his pressure was about 145/90 but it advanced to 175/100 after a difficult day, unless he had taken a sedative. It advanced likewise following worry —for example, about his cataracts (which had been removed). He was particularly anxious about his sleep, for which he took a sedative (Desbutal) nightly. His concern over hypertension seemed warranted, since his mother had died of hypertension, his father of a stroke (but without hypertension) and of six siblings, one brother suffered from angina and very high blood pressure. His eyes had been tense for years. He was allergic to many drugs and to other agents. Such was the picture which had led him to reduce his working hours to 4 per day.

In 1954 he was examined at the Mayo Clinic and I am indebted to Dr. D. A. Scholz for a report on the findings. The blood pressure was 160/90 without cardiac enlargement. Laboratory studies, including hemoglobin, leucocyte count, serology, urine porpyhrins, blood sugar, uric acid, serum-calcium and roentgenogram of the chest, were all normal. Grade 1 microhematuria was noted. The electrocardiogram revealed a left bundle branch block with an inverted P wave in lead III (present since 1945).

General examination on December 6, 1957 revealed a man of quiet demeanor, apparently in the midfifties, with steady gaze but with fidgets of the limbs. He spoke in restrained, low tones. He weighed about 180 pounds and his height was 68¾ inches. His blood pressure ("following a good night") was 148/83 lying, 140/87 sitting and 148/89 standing. The right tonsil was lobulated, but no pus could be expressed. The left had been removed. The tongue showed a light coating and the pharynx appeared to be chronically reddened. There was an operation scar over the gall-bladder region.

On January 9, 1958, electrocardiograph evidence of left bundle branch block was still present. A PA teleroentgenogram of the chest, with fluoroscopy, indicated abnormality in the form of the heart, seemingly due to left verticular enlargement and/or hypertrophy. On April 20, 1961, x-ray films indicated moderate degenerative osteoarthrosis of the thoracic spine.

The personal and the family histories plus the cardiac findings indicated a diagnosis of Early Essential Hypertension.

Effect on Blood Pressure

Instruction in self-operations control was begun January 6, 1958. The proposed schedule was 4 instruction periods on 2 days every 4 weeks, since his home was distant but he could visit Chicago periodically. A striking response to controlled rest appeared as early as January 8: before instruction his blood pressure was 130/80; after instruction it was 120/66.

By January 30 he reported that he had gained in sleeping time, averaging one hour more per night. On March 26 he slept 7 hours. On April 21 he reported that, in his yearly checkup, his pressure was found to be lower—140/86, compared with 150 to 155/90 in 1957.

Anxiety Controlled

On April 22, he reported diminution of his former anxiety over his business, although all four branches had been losing money for 5 months. On June 13 and July 10, he reported recurrence of insomnia. Even so, at the end of the instruction hour, his pressure for the first time in his known history was lowered to 114/64. He related that, whereas antihistaminic injections which he had received for an entire year before his present instruction had failed to bring relief from his allergic responses (including those to corn products and fermented drinks) and had, therefore, been discontinued, he was currently observing a reduction in these responses.

On December 10, 1958, he reported simply, "I no longer worry!" He was getting over his former habit of continually trying to solve his problems, which formerly had been his practice even at dinner. His family physician, who had not been informed of his course, on examining him looked incredulous, and asked, "What are you doing?" (Contrary to my desires, the patient had failed to keep the family physician informed.)

On January 16, 1959 he stated that distress from the eyes, including periodic eye-headache, had been absent for 8 months. However, tensing distress in the upper back, for which he had massages, was unrelieved.

Insomnia Lessened

Notwithstanding many recurrent bouts of insomnia, on April 10, 1958, he stated, "Following the instruction on speech con-

trol, I have been sleeping for the first time as long as 7½ hours."
In the annual check-up (by his local internist) of April, 1959,
his blood pressure, as compared with years prior to instruction,
was once more found to be lowered, namely, 140/80. He was
loathe to discontinue the nightly sedative. At about this time,
he was troubled by palpitation.

Ocular Headache

On November 4, 1959, he stated, "For 30 years I have had
eye headaches. I thought they would disappear after the
cataract operation, but they did not. Now (under this instruction) I have had no eye headaches for 1½ years. Since my sleep
has been poor for 35 years, I cannot expect to recover at once,
but this is my chief concern."

By this time he had increased his working hours from 4 to 6
per day. He was no longer troubled by palpitation, which had
lasted 6 weeks.

On April 18, 1960 he reported his observation that he no
longer tensed his limbs habitually. Now he had become able
to lie and sit still. However, he "still tensed his eye and speech
muscles constantly." Special training followed in these regions.
At this time he was learning to control his effort expenditures
at work.

On September 8, 1960, following a tense three-hour conference, with threats to bring suit, his pressure before instruction
was 154/80; after instruction, 142/86. This was the highest
figure he presented. (Because high figures never were found
in my clinic, I diagnosed this case as early essential hypertension only after careful consideration.)

How low can blood pressure be successfully reduced? On
June 6, 1961 before the hour of instruction, his blood pressure
was 106/78. (I have seen values even below these that were
persistent without medication in two patients initially with
systolic pressure above 200 and diastolic above 140.) He
reported that he felt good, and he appeared to be vigorous.

Relapse

On August 10, 1961 he reported a moderate relapse which
lasted 2 weeks. He attributed this to playing too much golf (a

game which he found to be tensing rather than relaxing) and to the discovery of an early carcinoma of the lip which was diagnosed and removed about July 5 or 6. (At about this time his brother died of carcinoma; he also had had high blood pressure—generally found to be about 200/100—for more than 25 years.)

He was last seen on March 20, 1962, when he reported improvement in sleep and appeared to be in excellent condition.

Lasting Improvement

On October 7, 1962, upon follow-up by phone, he reported that he felt in good health and was sleeping normally. He was practicing daily.

CASE 6. COMBINED PATHOLOGY AND
TENSION DISORDER, WITH UNRELIEVED PAIN

The patient was 57 years old, white, born in Ohio, married, with 2 children, president of a local insurance company. He was first seen on September 11, 1957. He complained of a generalized tension state which, he believed, produced spasm at the neck of the bladder, adding to his distress. He was continually disturbed by pain in the lower left abdominal quadrant, the left crotch and the left side of his back. Pain was marked also in his neck and shoulders. For 20 years he had suffered from constipation, with ribbon stools but little mucus. His appearance was one of disability from crippling pain, from which he said he was never free.

Some relief of the lower abdominal pain frequently followed injection of atropine sulphate at 6-hour intervals. Also somewhat responsive were distention and rectal flatus.

He was accustomed to taking mineral oil every second evening; in addition, he took Flexin for muscle spasm in the pyriform muscle and the back muscles, medication for increased blood cholesterol, vitamins and, about twice a week, Seconal or phenobarbital plus Pro-Banthine. However, the symptoms continued to be severe, notwithstanding the use of these drugs and the continuing attentions of a highly competent and interested urologist.

In 1927, an exploratory operation was performed at the Mayo Clinic for duodenal ulcer, for which the findings were negative; at that time, the appendix was removed. Prostatic symptoms soon led him to a urologist. At that time, also, spastic colitis was diagnosed. From 1927 to September 1, 1957, he said, "I have never been free from these painful symptoms and have been a constant patient at the offices of three specialists." He spoke at length of various forms of therapy that had been tried, including cortisone by mouth as well as injections of local anesthetics, frequent light massage for the pyriform muscle and heat, massage and exercise for the back muscles.

Physical examination disclosed a well-developed man, pleasant and composed yet evidently overalert. Lines attributable to anxiety and suffering appeared in his face and forehead. His pupils were round but overactive to light and accommodation. He weighed about 178 pounds and his height was 72½ inches. His temperature was 98.2 degrees, his pulse 78, and his blood pressure 112/70, when sitting. There were no important evidences of pathology, aside from two operation scars, marked tenderness fairly localized in the lower left quadrant and sharp tenderness on pressure on the left lobe of the prostate, which was not enlarged.

Diagnosis

Clinical laboratory examination disclosed chiefly highly spastic colon and esophagus (one-swallow method); low limb voltage leads in the electrocardiogram; and basal metabolic rates of minus 28 per cent and minus 24 per cent on two successive tests. Blood counts, Kahn test and thoracic and dental findings on roentgenograms were chiefly negative. Accordingly, our diagnosis was: Tension disorder, chronic insomnia, chronic fatigue, spastic alimentary tract (especially the colon), chronic prostatitis and arthritis (muscular rheumatism). (In 1957, the diagnosis of the Mayo Clinic had been: Lumbosacral disc syndrome; pyriformis syndrome; irritable colon.)

Instruction in self-operations control was begun on September 25, 1957. It was planned to see him once a week. On November 5, he reported that pain interfered with his daily practice, which also had been interrupted by a spell of influenza.

General Improvement

On June 13, 1958 he reported much general improvement, excepting the joint pains. However, he admitted that he had not practiced at home since the end of April. He lost much time each day commuting from his suburban home to the city. Also, he and his wife had gone to California for a stay of about seven weeks. (There his wife had broken an arm and was in an automobile collision.) His pyriform muscle was still painful but improved. Now he was able to play golf in moderation. On June 25, 1958 he appeared to have gained in general health. He said that people told him that he looked better. By July 7, his facies was unmistakingly less anxious and suffering. Again he commented that his friends noted the change.

On October 14 he said that in July he had been in a hospital for observation. The orthopedist had recommended operation for repair of the 5th lumbar disc, with transplant and fusion as well as removal of any osteitis that might irritate the pyriform muscle, but the patient had refused. His uric acid was found to be high. Massage has been continued but he has had no medicine except aspirin. He believes that local pain has diminished somewhat.

On November 20 I commented, "During instruction today, you did well!" "I sure did!," he replied. "I have been practicing and hoped you'd notice it!" On January 16, 1959, he stated that, thanks to what he had learned, he now found it "much easier to go to sleep." On that day drill was given in noting and relaxing the wrinkling and the frowning which had been his habit. On January 27, 1959 he complained of nausea, rectal flatus and fullness in the right hypochondrium. On examination the gall-bladder was palpably enlarged, soft and tender. There was also a tender spot on the abdomen on the left side, below and lateral to the umbilicus.

On February 27, 1959 he told of a recurrence of severe muscle pain in the piriformis, which, he said, previously had been improved. Although this persisted, on March 3 he stated,

"Otherwise, I feel a lot better!" A week later he added that people were saying, "You look younger each year!" However, he stated that he really objected to lying down in practice. Reply was made that this objection was really only an excuse for failure to relax as much as was necessary. He was failing to distinguish his tension state from the issue. What needed to be controlled was this tension state, without excuses.

Remission of Symptoms With Minimal Practice

As recounted above, here was a patient with combined pathology and tension disorder, suffering severely from unrelieved pain. Yet he did not practice or come for instruction regularly. After March 10, 1959 I did not see him again or hear from him until October 1, 1962. Then, to my surprise, he appeared once more to visit. Now, for the first time, he appeared to be perfectly well. The facial appearance was amazingly changed for the better. He said that his bladder symptoms (which he had ascribed to tension) were much improved, so that now he "sees the urologist only once a year, instead of very frequently"; that, in general, he was radically improved and "everybody thinks so" (although not 100% cured); that abdominal pain was much diminished, no longer requiring hypodermic atropine and recurring only if he became too tense; that constipation had diminished so that now he seldom took petrolatum, adding that flatus was infrequent now and distention was much reduced.

He said that he ascribed his improvement, in part at least, to the instruction. "It taught me that my symptoms were due —at least, in part—to tensions and, as I improved, I became more philosophical, realizing that everything did not have to be accomplished in a day." He attributed approximately all of the improvement in the colon to the instructive treatment and was sure that, without it, he would not have achieved relative freedom from his arthritic complaints.

He admitted that he did not practice sufficiently (only one half hour nightly) and had discontinued attendance because of unwillingness to practice. Now he desired to turn over a new leaf.

As this case illustrates, there are cases in which the technics are so badly needed for excess tension that some correction is made successfully with even a minimum of practice. (I recall the case of a well known pediatrician who never practiced, yet, he stated, in later years following his course, that he would never have survived the pressures and the anxieties of financial and other strains during the 1930 depression (presumably including the death of one son) if it had not been for instruction in progressive relaxation.)

CASE 7. MILD ANXIETY AND INSOMNIA
RELATED TO BUSINESS PRESSURES

The patient was an outstanding industrialist (white, American, married, having 2 healthy children). When he was first seen on June 8, 1960, he complained of moderate insomnia, fatigue, at times, and, especially, the necessity to *drive* himself—which he feared to do too hard lest coronary troubles result. He did not consider himself to be nervous or tense and had organized his business schedule to "avoid getting too jammed." At times, however, he became mildly anxious. He went to sleep promptly every night and slept well for several hours, but, thereafter, he awakened and tossed for about 3 hours until he fell asleep once more, but only for about 1 hour, after which he arose. There was some evidence of constipation but no history of digestive upsets. His parents, brothers and sisters were of "low pressure, rather than high-strung." His father was well at 87; his mother died of carcinoma at 83. His working hours generally were from 8A.M. to 4:30 P.M.

Efficiency the Real Aim

According to the history, here was a healthy, very high-powered executive of highest rating, well-organized in his habits, desirous of overcoming certain moderate symptoms in the interest of improved health and longevity. In our terms, however, the symptoms, particularly the necessity "to drive himself" that he complained of, indicated the need to improve his self-operations control in the interests of increasing his efficiency. Our aim would be chiefly to teach him to accomplish as much work with less tension-energy expenditure. He readily agreed to this.

The patient was a well developed man, genial, quiet mannered, soft-spoken but self-assured also. Physical examination disclosed that his height was 69 inches, his weight 172 pounds, his pulse 64, regular, his temperature 98° and his blood pressure 107/72, when sitting. There were no significant pathologic findings.

Clinical laboratory findings on urine, blood (including Kahn test) and roentgenography of chest and teeth were negative. The colon films and the esophagus test disclosed slight spasticity only.

Instruction in self-operations control was begun on July 5, 1960. Discussion covered the need to observe signals from effort-energy expenditure which derive from muscle spindles. It was explained that this is direct perception by the muscle sense; that in intact man muscle contractions are physiologic but the purpose is psychological; that going off with the power in any purposive muscle contraction may mean sacrifice or termination of the purpose. Differences between goal-living and self-operations control were noted (see Chap. 4).

The patient was given instruction concerning problem solving in business or other matters. Especially, he was informed that executives often blame the problems on the pressures, believing that their overefforts and anxiety are necessary, whereas, really, they are not.

At the end of July, 1960, following 8 periods of instruction, he said that he had begun to practice at being as relaxed as possible when walking and during business conferences.

Lessened Constipation and Insomnia

On September 2 he reported "amazingly much tension in his forehead all day long." On September 3 he reported that his symptoms of constipation and insomnia were lessened. His report offered evidence of freedom from therapeutic suggestion, for in it he commented frankly, "I do not know if this improvement is due to your treatment." I accepted this without argument.

On September 24, 1960 he went on a hunting trip on which he experienced a return of constipation. This, he stated, indicated that vacations do not in themselves reduce tension effectively. Now he realized better the importance of self-operations control.

On September 25, he was warned to remind himself many times a day to run his organism.

Anxiety Relieved

On September 29 he reported for the first time that he was no longer subject to anxiety. This had happened only after he had gained considerable skill in control of eye tensions with imagery.

On October 20 he reported experiencing a relapse followed by quick recovery. On November 2 it was noted that his jaws were held rigid continuously. He reported lessened fatigue. When driving, he now was accustomed to keep one arm and one leg relaxed (i.e., power off).

On November 15, when he was requested to go entirely off with eye plus speech muscle power, he reported success, adding that, for about 5 to 8 seconds, his mind was blank, without visual or speech imagination. Two days later he reported successful energy saving control during the strain of a meeting over which the chairman of the board presided.

On November 22 instruction in differential control was begun in the sitting posture. On December 16 he reported that, on the night before, he had been awake but relaxed from 3 A.M. to 5 A.M. "This was infinitely better than lying awake unrelaxed, as took place formerly."

On March 7, 1961 he reported that now he was sleeping fairly well.

On April 22, 1961 he reported an incidental spell of right sacroiliac pain (with negative roentgenograms) which responded to analgesics by mouth and hypodermic. At about this time he expressed "appreciation of the help he had received" and discontinued attendance. In all he had received 84 hours of instruction.

Somewhat more than a year later, I phoned in follow-up. He said that he was very well and had retained most of his gains, notwithstanding reduced hours of practice. The one exception was his sleep pattern, which was still improved but not as much as he would like. Special practices were prescribed by phone. On October 7, 1962 he reported that he had employed these practices with success and pleasure. I reminded him of the advantages which could result from resuming daily practice and he agreed fully.

CASE 8. TENSION DISORDER, HYPOCHONDRIA,
SPASTIC COLON

The patient, a businessman, 61 years old, married, with one child, white, born in the Midwest, was seen first on March 25, 1953. He complained chiefly of fullness in the epigastrium after eating, pyrosis, some eructation and flatus from rectum. His bowels moved regularly.

He dated the onset of the symptoms about 1944, when his father died after prostatectomy and a sister with carcinoma of the breast had died also. As far back as he could recall "any shock would catch him" (in the epigastrium).

Epigastric distress began about ½ to 1 hour after lunch or dinner. It was relieved by Tricheamalate. If he omitted medication, he might be awakened by the distress at night. Two years previous, he had begun a milk and cream diet, soon followed by soft food. However, he had never adhered to any diet rigidly; he ate all foods but felt less distress if he avoided excess of fats. Gall-bladder examination had proved negative 2 years ago, confirming prior examinations. He did not smoke, drank little and retired at a reasonable hour. Family history was negative. He was married in 1924. There had been one child with no other pregnancy.

Physical examination disclosed a well-developed man, about 70 inches in height and 169 pounds in weight. His hair was grizzled and he wore glasses. After pressure on his tonsils to test for pus he evidenced his excitability by regurgitating a fine yellow chyme. In the sitting posture, his pulse was regular at the rate of 84 and his blood pressure was 140/82. The pupils were very slightly irregular, but reacted normally. Otherwise there were no significant findings.

Diagnosis

X-ray pictures with dye tests disclosed a normally functioning gall-bladder without stones. Normal structure was found in the esophagus, the stomach, the duodenum, the small intestine (completely visualized) and the colon. However, the esophagus (by the one swallow test) and the colon were found to be spastic. The basal metabolic rate was minus 19 per cent on two successive tests. Many red cells were found on urinalysis, which otherwise was negative. Gastric analysis revealed free and combined HCl and total acidity, all low. There was no occult blood. Negative findings included those from blood smears and counts, the Kahn test, the electrocardiogram, fecal analysis and chest fluoroscopy. Moderate dextroscoliosis was found in the lumbar spine. A metal nail was in place through the greater trochanter neck and the head of the right femur, which appeared irregular in shape. My diagnosis was: Tension disorder; anxiety tension; hypochondria; spastic digestive tract; old operated healed fracture of the right femoral neck.

Weekly instruction in self-operations control was begun on April 1, 1953. As a rule, the patient attended and practiced regularly. Differential control in the sitting posture was begun on January 13, 1954.

During April, 1954, when his mother died, he reported that he bore up well, thanks to the training.

Anxiety Tension Control

On March 17, 1955 instructions, as on some previous occasions, concerned anxiety tension. "In prolonged efforts to think out a matter of concern, seeking relief from a problem hanging over you, you try to allay your anxiety. This is natural and instinctive, but it is not what you are to learn here. On the contrary, as you have experienced, the prolonged effort to relieve anxiety by reflection commonly prolongs the anxious state. You say, 'Ah, it isn't so bad! At any rate, I can overcome it.' And so, before you know it, you are lost in a host of reflections coupled with bitterness, depression and a feeling of weight and oppression in the chest and the abdomen. What you need to do, however paradoxical it may first appear, is to relax the very effort to allay your anxiety. To be sure, sometimes you need to find the answer to your problem; if so, do it and be done with it! It is important to have fears to prepare for the future, but you need to count the costs even so, for there can be too much of a good thing. In order really to apply the technic that you are learning, it is necessary to set out to go negative on your effort-patterns to resolve your anxiety."

On June 22, 1955 the patient was discharged. He had been taking no medicine. During previous months he had been reporting that he "felt very much relaxed" and was approximately free from his initial complaints and symptoms. "Now I can sit here for an hour, relaxed, without moving," he added significantly.

Follow-up

The patient was called by phone about 7 years later (on October 7, 1962). He reported that he practiced regularly and owed much to this. What he had learned and practiced gave him greater ability to get through difficult periods. However, he was still troubled by pyrosis.

CHAPTER **8**

Anxiety Tension
Control

Discouragement and Relapse

General instructions for applying self-operations control in the practice of medicine were stated in Chapter 5. Very much abridged accounts illustrative cases were given in Chapter 7. In the present chapter special instructions are added to achieve lasting results. We need to consider discouragement on the part of the patient—caused, perhaps, by return of anxiety or other emotion in the form of relapse—and the means to prevent or minimize these difficulties.

The course of chronic medical disorders, both functional and organic, (like that of love) commonly never—or seldom—runs smooth, even if eventual recovery ensues. Chronic medical disorders often are subject to relapse. Awareness of this often can prevent much needless concern. During the very first hours of instruction as a rule I draw a curve of possible progress before the patient in order to prepare him. (Fig. 6, page 140.) The abscissa represents time; the ordinate represents his symptom-tension levels.

"Assuming that we can represent these levels at the present day by a point high up and that the curve will fall to zero tension level at some future time, represented by another point on the zero axis (abscissa), we may ask ourselves whether this

139

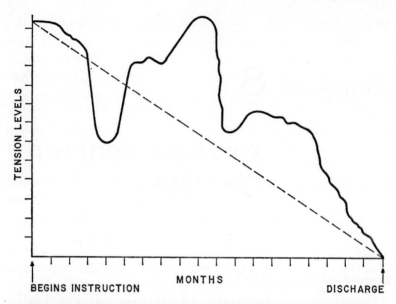

TENSION LEVELS

BEGINS INSTRUCTION   MONTHS   DISCHARGE

FIG. 6. Sample of a curve drawn for beginners to warn that improvement without relapses is not expected. They are told: Regardless of how great the improvement when discharged, there will be ups and downs in the course of treatment. There will be times of discouragement and relapse; but these offer indispensible opportunities to learn how to meet difficult moments.

hypothetical progress reasonably can be represented by a straight line? Shall we draw a straight line to represent that we expect your progress to make you 'better and better every day'? Obviously, this is extremely unlikely. It is reasonable to expect that like a stock-market curve when prices fall or a weather curve of daily temperature on the approach of winter, in your progress there will be ups and downs of the curve rather than a straight line."

As these matters are explained, the doctor may draw a curve roughly with ups and downs.

"The first marked rise of the curve, marking return of symptoms, may, of course, come at any time after the beginning of instruction, whether early or later. It is likely to be attended by some degree of discouragement. "Am I doing right?" "Is this the right treatment?" "Does the doctor really understand and is he interested?" These are examples of the manifold questions and doubts that may come to you, and, with them may come "reasons" for discontinuing instruction treatment. Be sure to discuss these with the doctor, if and when they arise."

After instruction of weeks or more, there may be a relapse worse than the original malady. "For many patients, to have begun to feel better and then to feel worse, is all the more discouraging." It is fair to inform the patient that, with progressing instruction, relapses tend to become briefer in duration, usually to be less severe and, at any rate, to disappear relatively quickly.

On the same occasion, it is of value to comment on sudden dips of the curve, signifying sudden diminution of symptoms. The patient may feel so good all of a sudden that he is prompted to discontinue treatment as no longer necessary.

"Forewarned is forearmed" against the two types of changes in the curve of progress, and the doctor should prepare his patient in advance, in this as in all other departments of chronic medicine where therapeutics are sufficiently advanced to warrant a possibly favorable prognosis.

Avoid Reassurance and Suggestion

It is important to repeat that best results through tension control are not attained through favorable prognosis, reassurance or, least of all, suggestion. Every patient tends to seek reassurrance. To be sure, if the prognosis from following a certain route of treatment is favorable, he should be told so. He comes to the doctor's office seeking favorable results, just as he makes a purchase of plane or railroad tickets in order to get somewhere.

Tension as a Source of Need for Reassurance

However, the tense, emotional patient often is a creature of hesitations, doubts and fears. Reassurance offers little more than temporary relief for the temperaments of most of us in this "age of anxiety." Tension control offers a tougher approach to reality. *It is necessary to make the patient realize that, as a rule, he is overtense at the moment he seeks reassurance and this is why he seeks it.* The instruction is "When you seek reassurance, look for tension-image patterns of emotion. On finding them, go negative where the tension appears!"

In plain words, the fearful patient needs to learn to observe the physiologic signals in which he engages without knowing it, for dreading consequences, he is engrossed wholly in the fearful meanings of these signals. What he needs most is not reassurance but drill in observation and selective control. He will do better, I believe, to learn this directed technic than to depend on golf or occupational therapy for diversion from his troubles.

No Concentration on Muscles

I wish to emphasize again that tension control methods do not work by distraction or diversion of the patient's attention from his troubles to his muscles. The patient is never directed to focus his attention on his muscles or on anything else as a means of diverting him from his anxiety.* On the contrary, the patient is taught that only a moment of attention is necessary and that, with practice, observation of tension becomes a matter of habit which is performed automatically with little if any, attention.

The experienced clinician can readily note the excessive winking, frowning and wrinkling of the forehead that takes place if the patient pays too much attention to any tension-act. Also, as can be noted, his eyes move as if to look steadily at the particular muscle group. The instructor tells the patient that he is being overtense! Attention, I have found, is always ocular in persons who have never been blind, whatever it may involve in addition.

Understanding this, the overattention can be corrected readily. This becomes easy after the eye region has received sufficient practice and eyes become relaxed. Then, as a rule, the

---

* One popular "teacher of relaxation" evidently failed to see this central point, for he had his pupils "concentrate on one big toe while relaxing."

improvement in the patient's tension-symptom rating becomes most clear, but, at this point, what obviously is taking place is inattention, not diversion of attention to muscles. The patient with relaxed eyes is ipso facto inattentive.

Hypochondria

The doctor should understand and be able to explain the difference between hypochondria and observation of tension-image patterns. Hypochondria is excessive attention to symptoms, along with constant complaining, and is known as "morbid introspection." Habits of morbid introspection are common in neurotic and other patients who visit the doctor often. The folly of the view that expressing complaints relieves them by letting them out like pus from an abscess is well illustrated by the fact that this class of patient constantly expresses his complaints and constantly seeks new ears for further expressions in the quest for reassurance and relief. Similarly, many chain-smokers often are heard to complain of their habits, but there is no evidence that complaining in itself reforms the habit.

Special Procedure for Chronic Anxiety: Reflect; Observe; Relax

Experience shows that in marked or chronic anxiety states, it is not sufficient for the patient to follow the simple rule, "Find the tensions and relax them." He should be informed repeatedly that this often proves to be insufficient. The relaxation may be *premature!* In such instances he begins to try to relax and without knowing it continues in his effortful reflections to solve the problems of how to resolve his difficulties. This combination is futile.

It is necessary, instead, to get him to do one thing at a time, namely, first, to reflect without relaxing; second, to observe his tension image patterns and then only to set out to relax these patterns.

Accordingly, he may be instructed to omit all relaxation as premature while taking Step 1, namely, sitting down for a half hour (or more, if necessary) to delineate the situation objectively. Every pilot of a plane or ship needs to know traveling conditions. He needs to know possible routes in order to select the best one. It is no different with the road of life. All of us can gain by taking an objective look at it. In self-operations control the task is to distinguish the road as sharply as possible from oneself, the instrument which is to be engineered over that road.

Likewise, the patient should defer relaxing on taking Step 2. This may require minutes or more of observation of his tension-image patterns which constitute his representing signals of the objective situation along with his impulses to respond for his welfare.

Only after having taken Steps 1 and 2 in succession is he prepared really to deal with his anxiety-tension responses. He can employ these responses up to the point where they lead him to a practical solution of his difficulties. Beyond this point, he should apply his control technics.

The patient should be instructed that the anxiety habit must be broken. Failure may occur repeatedly but, in the course of time, anxiety tension control can become a new habit, replacing the old wasteful habit of excessive, fearful reflection.

Example of Relapse

This example is taken from Case 5, whose abridged case history was recounted in Chapter 7, beginning on page 125.

During July, 1961, the patient suffered a relapse, but without return of high blood pressure. For two weeks he suffered from extreme fatigue, return of insomnia and of what he sensed as marked muscle tension in both forearms. He believed that the relapse had been triggered by excessive playing of golf in a club tournament, with attendant tension and strain not only of competition but also of social affairs in connection with the tournament. He added that generally he is much more interested in his business than in golf, but, for the time, the golf was paramount.

He believed that, to some extent, the relapse had been triggered by concern over a lesion of his lip which had been present for 2 years. His family doctor told him it was nothing but finally consented to his seeing a surgeon, who removed it on a diagnosis of carcinoma. A brother has been in the terminal stages of carcinoma, but he doubted that he himself had been greatly disturbed over this fatal outcome.

When he reported for instruction on August 10, 1961, the relapse had been on the wane, his symptoms diminishing, during the preceding 5 days. The instructions given to this patient are reproduced in the following section and may serve as an example of the general form for tension disorders, including also anxiety and other neurotic forms.

How To Handle Relapse

Realize that relapse is natural and can be expected after undue overexertion or nervous strain. Realize also that before you began instruction here, you habitually pursued goals and lived more or less instinctually, untrained as yet to observe effort-costs and to practice effort economy. A relapse is falling back into old habits; just as after breaking a smoking habit of many years, a person may readily fall back to old habits. Realize, then, that relapse is an expected hazard which provides you with an excellent opportunity to learn.

Realize that upon relapse, many people react with disappointment, discouragement or despondency. Becoming engrossed in their symptoms, they are seized with doubts and misgivings concerning the present methods, the treatment or themselves. (When he heard this, the patient responded, "Right as you can be! It raised doubts in my mind!")

These doubts tend to subside of themselves as the relapse wanes.

If the patient is to learn to run his organism during relapse and if the tendencies mentioned occur in relapse, he ought to be familiar with his tendencies during relapse so as to handle himself properly.

The relapse throws him back to an earlier stage of learning in which he became engrossed in his symptoms oblivious of the presence of tension and image signal patterns, that is, effort patterns to size up the difficult problems and his bad symptoms.

Thus thrown back to a stage of neglect of tension patterns and doubt, he becomes more or less helpless to set the stage for his own recovery—as helpless as he was originally before instruction, before he had ever learned to observe and relax effort-tensions.

If the patient has practiced with daily diligence, the relapse tends to pass away automatically. With passage of time, if he has had many months of instruction and observation of effort-tension and tension control have become habitual, the relapse tends to become briefer and less severe.

To recover more promptly from symptoms of relapse, you should revive not only your relaxing technic but also your powers of observation (for you have been acting blindly without knowing it).

In addition, you should follow these rules which enable you to realize the actual situation more clearly.

1. During relapse, sit down—perhaps as long as one half hour—and, *without relaxing*, state the issue: The issue is, "I am exhausted and I am not sleeping." This is true or this is false. Or the issue is, "I have had a lip cancer."

2. Again without relaxing, find the location and the types of your tensions and your images.

3. Following these two steps in succession, which you should have taken without relaxing, you should now proceed to relax the specific tension patterns which you identified. Remember that, if you do not take the two steps first, the relaxing will be premature. Therefore to render yourself adequate, you are first to distinguish clearly between yourself as instrument and the roads you will need to follow just as a pilot prepares for a difficult flight. Second, you are to examine the tension-image signals patterns by which you represent to yourself your problems and in which you are making efforts to find the answer. Third, and last in order, you are to discontinue your excessive wasteful effort tensions to solve the problem. This is sacrifice for your own good, your own efficiency in the long run.

CHAPTER 9

Anxiety Tension, Cardiac Neurosis (Persistent After Psychoanalysis) and Coronary Insufficiency

The patient was male, white, 34 years of age, married (with two children), a brilliant and distinguished professor. He was first seen on October 19, 1957. He complained of constant pressure in the chest and throughout the body; faintness at times (diminished on bowing his head); insomnia; fatigue and evening exhaustion; palpitation after eating, extreme irritability and slight dyspnea. Often he felt himself trembling. If he failed to sleep, there was micturition once.

Course of Psychoanalysis

Five years earlier, the patient began a systemic psychoanalysis for possible precursors of the present symptoms. He would become blocked after starting to carry out certain brilliant conceptions and then shift to a different enterprise. He discontinued analysis because it failed to yield therapeutic

147

results, although, he asserted, it gave him better insight and better life-goals. Commonly, he averaged about three hours per week in analysis, but, often, there were interruptions, so that the average was a little reduced. He was analyzed by a disciple of a distinguished analyst, who later on, sent him to conclude his analysis with a woman physician.

He related that, before analysis (and up to the present time), he had been spreading himself "between diverse academic disciplines and between academic and practical responsibilities—spreading so much that life became a constant set of deadlines to meet, deadlines of articles, of books, committee meetings, consulting assignments, hearings and speeches. I turned down very few requests that were made of me, always taking on task after task. During some of these tasks, especially those which involved writing, I would get myself caught in blocks. I would start off in very satisfactory fashion and suddenly feel myself inhibited in completing a major writing task. It was largely this reason, coupled with my own interest in psychoanalysis, that led me to begin my analysis 5 years ago. In the course of the analysis, I took on more and more responsibility. I worked closely with many of the top industrialists in the United States and have taken on more and more research projects, more and more editing tasks, more and more writing and speaking commitments and more and more commitments of almost every kind. Every week there are all sorts of deadlines to be overcome rather than the pleasant prospect of a normal working arrangement. So far, the years of analysis have not been very successful in dealing with the problems which I just described. Possibly, the insights of analysis will help me in the years ahead, but I don't know. I have grown to understand some of the conflicting drives within me, such as the drive, on the one hand, of the only child who wants all things for himself, who can't bear to give anything up. On the other hand, there is the child who has to prove himself and the child, overprotected by the widowed mother, who wants to assert his manhood and does this by taking on seemingly Herculean tasks. Psychoanalysis has given me considerable insight as to why I react this way, but, as yet, it has not enabled me to act differently. It was a terrible strain on me to complete one book; I had blocks which made me hesitate to put out chapters, words and pages. My analysis suggested that much of this block came from my fear of competition. Unconscious material through analysis suggested that I was very much concerned about exposing myself. If my ideas and views were written, I would be subject to criticism. I was fearful of that criticism and the fear was in many ways the unconscious fear of castration.

"In the unconscious I was afraid not only of some retaliation but also that the writing would be a hurtful act toward other people, with the concept of the pen being mightier than the sword; and, for a number of reasons, there was a certain lack of acceptance on my part of aggression and competition. My unconscious rejection of aggressive competitive action was coupled with a fear of retaliation and seemed to result in a block in writing. Much of the block still remains. Another theme in the analysis was the unacceptability of my own desire to be taken care of, to enjoy myself and to be passive. I reacted so much that I gradually moved into a life pattern with no recreation, no vacation and none of the pleasures of leisure time. The one thing I can reasonably hope for as an end-product of analytic work is gradually to be able to cut down the number of tasks I take on, thus sparing more time for pleasurable nonwork pursuits. However, in the year immediately ahead, there is no prospect of being able to get out of major responsibilities. I feel that my problem is how to fulfill those tasks without the terrible physical pressure and wear and fatigue which I feel within myself. I find myself so weary these days that it is hard to be coherent. I must give a talk soon and I must prepare the speech; otherwise I would sound like an utter fool. I would just get up and ramble incoherently.

"The drive within me to take on task after task seems under analysis to stem from a number of sources, one of which was a kind of rejection of an image of myself as a small child, over-protected by my mother, a passive dependent wanting very much to be a strong masculine figure. Since the child was brought up without a male figure in his life, the result has been that he took on various kinds of tasks to prove and assert his own masculinity, his own importance, and, at the same time, he rejected the receptive drives within, the urge to play, to enjoy himself and others. All this was coupled with a certain type of narcissism, too—narcissism of the only child, who wants all things for himself and can't bear to give up the glories which come incidentally with these tasks, including the status symbols and the praise. The drive to overwork is a combination of factors of that kind."

"Has it appeared to you as if your conduct was on a semi-compulsive basis?"

"Compulsions arise from the characteristics I have just described. Incidentally, I think the worries I complain of are felt by capable people in many fields, including business executives, those who are obliged to run not only their own business affairs but endless civic affairs as well."

He states that he got much inspiration from his mother but also bears much resentment, which he knew of before the analysis. "I very rarely see my mother these days. We quarrel terribly."

Earlier History

The patient was born in New York City. His father was an agricultural engineer, his mother, a school teacher. When he was fairly young, his father died and he was brought up by his mother and, to a large extent, his grandparents and a bachelor uncle, who provided much of the masculine companionship which he had as a child. His mother encouraged him to read rather than to use his body. "She was fearful of dangers, including athletics, and projected some of her own anxieties on to me. As a child, I had very few friends, was very close to my family and read tremendously. I had many periods of illness and I was much isolated, without feelings of companionship with other children. Not until I got to college did I begin to expand my social contacts and become close in a meaningful way to boys and girls of my own age. My intellectual interests were various and I jumped constantly from field to field, from classical languages to engineering and to other subjects in between, finally finding a certain field which synthetized my interest in economics and engineering. At the age of 24 I was made assistant professor in a large university. At 29 I was assigned to a very choice academic post. I had other civic responsibilities. In these past years I have been engaged in many national matters.

"At the age of 21 I met the woman who was to become my wife. We were married when we were both about 23 years old. Her field of interest is the same as mine. Of late, I have been extremely irritable toward her and the two children, a boy 4 years of age and a girl 2½ years of age. I have been extremely difficult to live with. Often, following an outburst, I have felt extremely guilty. She has been extraordinarily patient. My son seems to have many of the psychic characteristics which belong to me. He is fearful of animals and of getting hurt, tends to play by himself and virtually teaches himself to read with no formal assistance from his parents. His small sister is very different, much less fearful, much more outgoing, much less interested in abstractions and much more interested in people. She is much more voluble.

"I have had no vacation in the last 5 years and have become increasingly fatigued. The chairman of a department of medicine advised me to slow my efforts. The greatest strain I have experienced dates back these last 3 years. At times, one and a half years ago, I felt myself getting faint at meetings or during particular stress. A routine check-up gave no indication of the cause. The cardiogram was negative. During the last few weeks I frequently have felt faint. This has occurred particularly in periods of stressful meetings. After a very important meeting recently, when I had to present much material to convince people, I felt I would faint several times in the cab after departure. I was pleased with the success which I met but felt near collapse. I met one of the principles again and, thereafter, I was completely exhausted and went home to bed.

I was able to fall asleep immediately, but, as usual, in recent experience, I was not able to stay asleep. Sometimes, before going to bed, I take Seconal as an aid to sleep, but I do not find it very effective. Sometimes I have taken Atarax tablets. So far as I can see, they have had little or no effect. In the last 2 or 3 years I have had much more difficulty in breathing. Perhaps this comes from a complete lack of physical exercise coupled with aging. Even when I walk at a moderate pace, I often find myself short of breath. Often I am conscious of the pounding of my heart—for example, all of today. I am particularly conscious of this when I feel great stress and strain. Occasionally, there is diarrhea, usually with one or two movements. At other times I may be constipated. As a rule, this lasts no more than two days."

Sexual History

Onanism began at the age of 12 and continued to the age of 21. Heterosexual activity occurred about four or five times weekly before marriage. There have been no extramarital relations.

General Examination

On March 14, 1958, general examination disclosed an alert, vigorous, dark-haired man whose appearance corresponded to his age. His speech was clear and, as a rule, he was smiling. At times, when he spoke about his heart, he evinced signs of concern. In the sitting posture, his pulse was 80 and regular, his blood pressure, 110/70, his temperature, 98.2°, and his respiration normal. His height was 5 feet 7½ inches, his weight, stripped, was 161 pounds. The pupils were highly active to light. His eyes and nose showed no pathology. There were various amalgam inlays in his teeth. The tonsils had been removed, and no pus could be expressed from any remnants in the fossae. Findings in the tongue, the pharynx, the neck and the entire thorax, including the heart, were negative. There was no enlargement of the auricle and no other signs of pathology. The findings in the abdomen (including the liver and the spleen), the genitalia and the limbs were also normal. There were two hairy moles and some lentigo on the patient's back. The patellar reflexes were lively but other deep reflexes and the cranial reflexes showed no pathology. The rectal examination, including that of the prostate, was negative.

Laboratory Examination

In the laboratory examination, a teleoroentgenogram suggested slight left ventricular enlargement. The 5 minute esophagus film indicated moderate spasticity. The colon was found to be highly spastic in a film made 18 hours after the ingestion of a barium meal. The electrocardiogram showed low voltage in the limb leads and the PR interval was 0.20 seconds, the extreme upper limit of normal. The basal metabolic rate on two successive tests was -11 and -12 per cent. The blood counts were essentially negative; hemaglobin was 14 Gm. per cent. Negative also were the results of Kahn test, urinalysis, sputum examination and dental roentgenograms.

Diagnosis

The diagnosis was: Cardiac neurosis, tension disorder, early coronary insufficiency; chronic fatigue; spastic digestive tract.

INSTRUCTION ON SELF-OPERATIONS CONTROL

OCTOBER 19, 1957. Instruction was begun on self-operations control by the self-engineering methods, as follows: "You have said, 'The one thing I can hope for as an end-product to analytic work is gradually to be able to cut down the number of tasks I take on and devote some of the time free from those tasks to pleasurable nonwork pursuits.' We shall not endeavor to explore or to speculate on genesis of the difficulty mentioned; we shall consider it as a present difficulty to be understood and attacked directly. Therefore, our efforts will not be chiefly to inquire into how the dust got into the room but, rather, to sweep it up and prevent recurrence."

Instruction was given concerning the nature and the operation of neuromuscular controls in the muscle spindles, which were compared with the operation of manipulatory controls on the dashboard of a motor-car and, also, with the wall-switch for the electric light in the room. The patient was informed that the human organism contains no such neuromuscular on-and-off control switch. For example, when the left hand is bent back at the wrist, energy is expended so long as this action continues. To discontinue, no switch-off takes place; the individual merely ceases to expend the energy of contraction and the bending discontinues.

Goal living vs. Use of Neuromuscular Controls

Goal living was discussed in detail, including the role of instincts, parental education, goals acquired by contact with other children and, later, in nursery school, grammar school, high school and colleges, and of goals acquired by general reading as well as association with others. In contrast with this, the possibility of learning to run one's organism as one learns to run a motor-car was discussed. The patient was informed that it is impossible to be anxious if, at the same time, one is sufficiently relaxed.

Fails To Understand Instructions at First

Instruction this day was devoted to the control musculature of the left arm. The patient appeared to be disturbed and distraught and evidently did not grasp the instruction fully. As he lay down in practice, with the book under his left wrist so as to enable him on instruction to contract the triceps musculature, he was instructed to go negative while I left the room. Instead, he pushed the book away. Instruction included practice on progressive tension and relaxation of the right arm musculature. There were two periods of instruction.

Overanxious To Help and To Understand

NOVEMBER 15, 16, 17, 1957 (4 periods). The patient stated that during the previous week he had a cold followed by what was diagnosed as Bell's Palsy. The paresis has been disappearing rapidly. Instruction was devoted to the left lower limb.

Instead of relaxing completely when the doctor moved a limb, the patient tensed to help. He was importunate, informing the doctor that his learning habits require him to understand each point, rather than merely to learn how to manipulate.

Reports Improvement

DECEMBER 13, 14, 1957 (4 periods). The patient said, "I can't tell you how much better I feel than when I began treatment!" He said that he had an important meeting for tomorrow evening and was nervous about it. He was instructed as follows:

Why It Is Always Easy To Relax

The nervous person fails to relax because he has habits of doing things the hard way. He lacks the know-how to relax and, commonly, has perhaps not even heard of the subject. However, it can be truly said that it is easy not to be tense or nervous. To come to this conclusion it is necessary first to agree on the use of the terms hard and easy. In the present connection the term hard may be defined as something that requires the application of energy. Then, to make efforts, involving muscular contractions, by definition is hard to the extent that energy of muscular contraction is required. In contrast, not to make an effort, simply to go negative, by definition evidently is easy. The nervous person does not relax because he does things the hard way and has habits of automatically making excess efforts in order to secure postural or other forms of comfort.

Angina

During the foregoing 4 weeks the patient had some chest disturbance which led him to have a cardiogram. This was reported negative. On the evening of December 12, he became angry and had a feeling as of clutching in the chest followed by palpitation. Instruction concerned tension patterns and controls of the musculature of the right lower limb and the back.

Coronary Insufficiency

JANUARY 11, 12, 1958. The patient appeared to be emotionally upset, describing chest symptoms and panic concerning them. He had had a roentgenogram of the gallbladder taken by some other physician. When I examined him, the findings were negative for gallbladder pathology. However, I told him, "We cannot rule out coronary insufficiency. Indeed, your symptoms suggest it to some degree." He was instructed in muscles of the back and the shoulders, and in left and right pectoral muscles.

Improvement in Appearance

FEBRUARY 7, 8, 1958. The patient had practiced and had become more conscious of his body. He looks alert, fit and cheerful and his eyes appear well directed during conversation. He had reduced his weight to some extent. Instruction was devoted to the neck, the forehead and the brow regions.

Anginal Pain

MARCH 13, 14, 1958. The patient had been traveling much of the time. He was "catching up" on matters which, formerly, he had been postponing. He had various types of symptoms from the chest, the most disturbing of which was pain below the left nipple, as if a pencil were pressed moderately over that area, but with occasional feelings of "squeeze" in the same region. At other times, he felt constriction in the center of the chest, just below the throat. He reported that practice at relaxation had diminished these symptoms for a short time only. "Practice would slow me down; thereafter, the same symptoms would return. Then I also began to get increasingly frightened. I read an article in the New York Times on coronary disease and was in panic."

Instruction Aided on Viewing Oscilloscope

A lesson was given while the patient was connected with the neurovoltmeter, so that he could observe electric patterns of tension. He was instructed in relaxing the eyelid and the eye muscles.

Angina Lessened

MARCH 27, 1958. Distress or pain was much reduced during practice of relaxation. Symptoms included (1) a muscular fatiguelike feeling, precordial in extent and locality; (2) a squeezing stress (he claimed that this was his own spontaneous description); (3) radiating pains in the left shoulder and the left upper arm with weakness and, sometimes, also with squeezing.

Thyroid Medication Instituted

Since low basal metabolic rates had been determined and his blood pressure was low (namely, values such as 94/80 or 94/70), thyroid medication (gr. ½ b.i.d.) seemed to be justified. Instruction again was related to eye muscles. The patient observed a pen moving back and forth before his eyes; later, he was asked to imagine doing so at various rates and, also, to imagine seeing other objects, noting the feeling of tense visual muscles.

Evidence of Panic

When he had been lying for about one half hour during one period, I was out of the room. Upon my return I found him sitting up, his face tense, his eyes fearful, with every external evidence of panic. He stated that he had felt his heart pounding and had been very much emotionally disturbed. He was permitted to sit and relax a short time before resuming the technical period of instruction.

Disturbed by Angina

APRIL 24, 25, 1958. The patient reported that he had not done well in practice during the last few weeks. He had been greatly disturbed by pains in the chest. When he misses appointments, as he did this morning, he becomes irritated. On being requested to imagine various matters including "A child walking by," he stated, "I think I was able to imagine . . ." I interrupted him to say, "We are not asking you about your ability. Please imagine just as you would have imagined ten years ago. What we want is observation, not a statement about your ability." Instruction was begun on the musculature of the jaws, the cheeks, the lips and the tongue.

In view of my diagnosis of coronary insufficiency (not for therapy of anxiety), he was advised to diminish his hours of consultative work and did so.

JUNE 26, 27, 28, 1958 (4 periods). Instruction on the speech musculature was continued.

Instruction in Care of the Heart

SEPTEMBER 18, 1958. Prolonged instruction was given to enable the patient to take care of his heart. He had learned to recognize and pay sufficient heed to tensions which indicate that he is expending his energy in one or another muscular region. He was to learn to avoid excess expenditure in whatever he did, applying only those energies which are needed in order to complete his task successfully. He was to continue regular practice at relaxation procedures lying down. He was to observe special precautions when he had distress. At such times he was not to run or walk fast. When he could sense muscular fatigue, he was to diminish his efforts accordingly on such occasions.

OCTOBER 17, 1958. Instruction was devoted to the speech musculature and imagined speech.

Daily Job Productivity Increased

MARCH 27, 1959. Electrical recording was performed on this date. He stated that he had been very busy, but, in view of the suspicion of coronary insufficiency, he had cut down considerably on his former activities. He had traveled to the Orient for professional purposes. Chest pains had become rare, while his daily job productivity had increased as a result of the technic during the last 3 months. He practiced on most days, but had missed some. He had been devoting his practice mostly to the limbs and stated that he believed that he had not yet mastered the head region. However, he practices in terms of the control method. Review of the musculature of the trunk region was given.

APRIL 3, 4, 1959. Electrical recording was repeated once more. Instruction concerned the musculature of the shoulder region.

APRIL 29, MAY 27, JUNE 25, JULY 23, 1959. Instruction was continued in the method of control, with practice particularly on the head and the neck musculature.

Differential Control Begun

SEPTEMBER 16, 17, 1959. Differential control was begun in the sitting posture with instruction devoted to the musculature of the arms.

NOVEMBER 12, 1959. The patient appeared to be very well; instruction was devoted to the left lower limb.

Free From Original Symptoms

DECEMBER 10, 1959. The patient had neglected practice to some extent but continued to appear well and to be free from emotional strain. Likewise, he had had no further chest symptoms.

JANUARY 7, 8, 1960 (4 periods). The patient had been well except for some symptoms not related to his original complaints, namely, a little stiffness in the right knee and a little pain in the groin. On his failure to complete a manuscript on January 1, as per schedule, he had sensations of tightness in the chest, but this aroused no concern. He reported great improvement but had been irregular in attendance for instruction. Now he discontinued instructive treatment and engaged in overseas consultation.

MARCH 9, 1961. The patient continued to be free from anxiety about his heart. While he still had chest symptoms, he was much less concerned about them. Pressure sensations no longer were constantly present in the chest, but it was "rare when I don't feel some." "I have been free from palpitation after meals." "However, recently my heart-beat sometimes has seemed somewhat irregular after I have been lying down a while. Upon change to an upright position, it often becomes regular again." "I have had no recurrence of feeling faint, except on one very trying occasion when I had to fly to California to expel a person from a society for unethical behavior." "I sleep well and much and have no shortness of breath." "I have been free from the spells of diarrhea alternating with constipation, of which I originally complained." "I have been much calmer, much less irritable." "I continue to have less consultative work, as you directed; but I still have a full schedule." "My failure is lack of diligence in practice, for I do not follow the daily instructions and practice only 2 hours per week."

Evidently, the instruction had succeeded in freeing him from anxiety. However, he was not entirely free from symptoms of coronary insufficiency. His practice had diminished these symptoms, but he was neglecting to practice five days a week. Believing that he had become too complacent, perhaps too free from concern about his heart, I urged him to practice one hour daily.

Follow-up

In follow-up by phone on September 28, 1962 the patient stated that he continued to be well and was working very hard, including during the summer. "Some symptoms appear moderately, such as tightness in the chest at times," he adds, "but they do not disturb me!" He said that he practiced about one half hour 3 times a week after getting to bed. I urged him to practice every day, but to do so during the day in order to get full benefit. He expressed determination to do so.

CHAPTER 10

Anxiety Control
Taught Quickly

As I have pointed out, anxiety control is basically an educational process; therefore, it seemed probable that it, too, could be taught effectively even in a very much abridged course. The following two reports are offered to illustrate that this can be done in suitably selected cases. The reports are designed to present data of interest to scientific clinical investigators. In addition, a verbatim account of instructions and responses may furnish useful examples to practitioners who may desire to meet difficult cases briefly. For clarity of exposition I shall edit somewhat and shall change the order in which instructions were given in the first three sessions.

Case 1. Anxiety with Homicidal Obsessive-Compulsion

History of Complaint.

The patient was 31 years of age, white, female, Irish-American, born in California, married, with four children. She was an attractive, energetic woman. When she was first seen on April 1, 1956, she complained of anxiety and fears of at least 11 years duration. She feared that she might kill one or more of her four children; therefore, she took pains to keep knives, scissors, razor blades and other tools out of sight and reach. In this her husband, a worker of Italian descent,

161

cooperated. She feared insanity and blindness. When she ascended to high places, she experienced dread of suicide. She often experienced panic on leaving her home. When she shopped, she felt uncomfortable. She did not like to go out but forced herself to do so.

During the past 2 or 3 months, fears had increased. She had suffered from nausea and forced her food down with no enjoyment. Consequently, she had lost 15 pounds in weight. Diarrhea had been marked, with 3 or 4 movements per day. Otherwise, her only complaint was of slight postnasal drip, which had been present for years.

Her housework and children occupied her time. She did not drink.

She recalled no previous ailments and had never visited a doctor before the time that anxiety-fear set in 11 years earlier. At that time, her tonsils and appendix were removed. In 1955 she had been operated on for tubal pregnancy.

Marital and Family Histories

She was married in 1946. Her children were 9, 8, 7 and 4 years old, respectively, of whom the second and the fourth were boys. They were well, but the eldest was very nervous. Her husband, also, was well.

Her father who was 50 years of age, was a habitual alcoholic and had suffered from "several nervous breakdowns." Her mother, who was a little younger, was quite well and not nervous. Both parents were born in America.

Her fears had begun about 1 year before marriage. Her account follows:

Onset and Course

"I went to school with my husband and we were engaged at the time. Later, he was away, overseas, but I was not worried about that. I was sick that winter with colds and earaches. My mother took me to the doctor then. That's when I began to get headaches in the back of my head. I thought it might have something to do with my mind. I didn't tell anyone about this fear. You asked what suggested it. One night I heard my parents talking about my uncle having a nervous breakdown. He insisted upon the doctors putting him away, but they laughed at him and told him to go home and forget it. My doctor told me that my headaches might come from bad tonsils. When I had the tonsils out and the headaches didn't go away, naturally, I thought there must be something the matter with my mind.

"I went to Florida for a vacation with a girl-friend after my husband had sent me some money. I felt better until I came home again, and then, inside of 2 or 3 weeks, it [the fear] started all over again. Of course I still said nothing to no one. My husband and I married and I got pregnant immediately.

"Then the fears really started to bother me and I went to a psychiatrist. He told me I was perfectly normal, and that it was just a fear that I'd get over and I should go home and forget about it. Instead, I just got another one, the fear of suicide. During the first 3 or 4 years of our marriage, I had these fears and I was a nervous wreck constantly. Then I went to a doctor in San Francisco and he helped me a little bit. He said that they were fears and I must learn to go against them and to forget about them. It seemed to help for a little while, but then it turned into a permanent thing. As soon as I would get nervous and upset about something, I would immediately get fearful and I'd put this fear on to something.

Suggestibility and Phobias

"I could read something in the paper or hear something, and, before you know it, I'd be putting that fear to myself. That's the way it always seemed to happen with me. That's what it is up to now. I still haven't had any relief from them. I keep getting them. This one here, this one of blindness I have now, is terrible. I think of it constantly all day long. I can't get free of it. I just feel that, out of a clear blue sky, I'm going to lose my sight and then I get panicky. I want to run somewhere—but I don't know where I want to run. I don't like to be left alone, but I am. My children go to school and my husband goes to work. I feel it could happen to me, even on the street.

"When I picked up Dr. Gutwirth's book a couple of months ago, I thought I would try to help myself. The book had a lot of sense. I thought I was accomplishing a little bit with it, but I couldn't seem to control the thoughts when I lay down to relax. I could relax to a certain degree within the thoughts. I seem to be a little worse. In other words, when I lie down and have time to think I seem to be a little worse. Then I thought I was feeling a little better and, then, 3 or 4 days ago, I read this piece in the paper about neurotics and blindness and paralysis, and that fixed it up good. I told the doctor about this fear I had, and he said blindness is purely physical.

"The fear of blindness began when I was in the hospital having my last baby. There was a woman in there and her daughter had come to see her. I think she was a nervous breakdown—I don't know. But her daughter confided to me that her mother had had a fear of blindness for quite a while and that she was in there for a rest.

Fear of Suicide

At this time, and any time I go to the hospital, I always have that fear of heights from way back when I had the fear of suicide. Every time I'd go to the hospital I had this fear and I'd say nothing to no one, but, all the while I was in the hospital, I'd be under constant strain for fear of the window. All the rooms are up high there, and I always felt that I'd jump out if I didn't watch myself. Then this woman started telling me about her mother and her fear of blindness and that's when the idea first got into my mind, but it didn't bother me too much then—it did a little bit, but I was able to overcome it.

"My fear of hurting people came right after the fear of suicide began. From fear of hurting myself, I had a fear of hurting someone else, namely, the children. I might turn on the gas and kill everybody. As I had that fear, I began to get a fear of sharp instruments or things. It all came from the one thing —fear that I'd pick it up and hurt someone with it. Then I used to put everything sharp away where I couldn't find it—although I think that must have been from a long way back, because, when my father was drinking, he used to come in and say he was going to kill my mother. He'd say he was going to do something terrible. And even the gas stove then—I used to wait until he went to sleep and then I would hide everything he could use to hurt anyone in the house with and make sure the gas was all shut off. I know I used to be a nervous wreck then. It was terrible. So I don't know whether that had anything to do with it or not, but I don't know why I should have the fear of hurting someone in my own family."

"When did the fear of your mind being wrong subside?"

"To a certain degree after I spoke to the doctor 9 years back."

"Then the fear of hurting someone began and ended when?"

"I had the fear of suicide next, and after I told the doctor about that, he said, "No, that's a fear of doing something; not that you would do it"; but I still had it inside. But I kept telling myself, "He knows better than I and not to argue with a mind that knows better than my own." And then that subsided a little bit. Off and on, as I would get nervous, I would get these fears back to a certain degree. They would always come back. If I would be feeling tense or nervous about something, and I'd see something sharp, I would get the feeling or thought of it, but I was able to subside. That would be about 3 or 4 years ago."

"Then?"

"Then this fear of blindness when I was in the hospital with the baby! That was 4 years ago and has not subsided. It bothered me only off and on. It came to me last year when I was ill, when I had the operation. I had to be in the hospital then, too. After I got out of the hospital I was very, very nervous. For about 3 or 4 months I seemed to be able to pull out of it, but, evidently, I didn't.

Analyst Visited

I went to a psychoanalyst twice. This was just recently—January, in Newark—Dr. L. He said I must be punishing myself for something. He said that I must have some guilt in me from back sometime and that I do these things like sticking pins in me or something. I couldn't seem to see it. I thought, "Well, maybe I did do something, but everybody does something they're ashamed of in their life." Then these women that I met there. The second time, they had a group meeting and this woman was there. She's been going for a year and she seemed no better at all. She had a fear of going out on the street even and her husband was still picking her up after a year's time. And I said to myself, "If this woman couldn't get cured in a year's time, then this is not right."

Early History

"Was there anything from your early childhood that would have any bearing?"

"No."

"No special sexual history before marriage?"

"Yes."

"To what extent? Intercourse?"

"No, almost to the point, but not quite there. I did pet a little bit with other fellows but nothing serious."

"Was that something that would, in the words of the analyst, arouse a guilt feeling?"

"Well, maybe at the time, I was a little guilty about it, because I tend to be a shy person; but, looking at it from my viewpoint now, I see so many people do the same thing that I don't feel I should feel guilty about it.

"I was graduated from high school when 18 years old."

Examination

General physical examination disclosed a well developed handsome woman who appeared to be of the age stated. There were no marked pathologic findings.

It was agreed that she would receive about 10 hours or more of instruction divided into 1-hour periods at approximately monthly intervals. Between the periods, she was to practice at home every day for at least 1 hour, following printed instructions on cards which would be given to her. There would be no promises of recovery, no reassurance, but only the teaching of how to manage her organism (self-operations control). Eventually, the course was prolonged to 14 hour-periods.

Course of Instruction, Self-Operations Control

APRIL 1, 1956: INSTRUCTION PERIOD 1. You asked, "Would you really go blind if you're worried about it enough?" I replied that you were seeking reassurance and that I do not plan to include reassurance. Reassurance consists of efforts to relieve your various fears. *Instead, you are to learn a lot about the efforts you make when you are having anxiety and fears.*

Let's begin with the beginning. Fear of going insane involved efforts to avoid going insane."

"To avoid going insane I wanted to help myself. That's why I went to the doctor. I wanted him to tell me if I was insane and how not to be if I was."

"What happens when you get reassurance that you're not going insane?"

"Then I get worried about something else."

"What about the weapons when you fear you might hurt somebody? What about the efforts then?"

"Well, I would hide things, like sharp instruments. I would feel that I had to hide those to protect whoever was around."

"So, your very nervousness was efforts, wasn't it?"

"Yes."

"Efforts to protect, efforts to avoid—and, now, this fear of blindness consists of efforts to avoid what?"

"To avoid hearing about it or reading about it, or knowing anything about it that would tell me it could happen to me."

"So that if we were to treat you by reassurance, what would happen?"

"I'd probably find something else to worry about."

"Provided that you got rid of the fear you have now. So it's very clear to you that when a person is nervous, it isn't merely that he is seeking protection and security, but the nervousness consists of efforts toward security. That's why he's nervous.

He's trying to protect himself. The efforts needn't be very uniform, consistent or successful, and they needn't be harmonized, integrated, working along with each other successfully. On the contrary, the nervous person may be trying to do three different things at one moment."

"That's me; I'm worrying at one time and doing something else and thinking about my fears, doing the housework; I'm doing three or four things at a time. I find that I don't do anything really too good."

"So then you see, one of the things we plan to do—in fact, the chief thing we plan to do—is to relax the efforts towards security."

"That's what I'm trying to do; I'm trying to be secure!"

"We're going to try to show you how not to try to be secure and . . ."

"In that way I will be secure."

Efforts and Effort Control

"Our program consists of showing you how to recognize when and where you're tense, including when you're nervous and fearful. It consists of showing you that when you're nervous or tense, when you're fearful, you're making an effort and that the easiest thing in the world is *not* to make the effort. You're working then for security. I want to show you how not to do that work, which really is easier than doing it. The easiest thing in the world is not to be nervous. There's nothing easier because it involves no work. That is what you mean by ease, is it not? Effort is work. Every act which you perform from morning till night—whether physical or mental—can be regarded as an effort of your organism. You are here to learn to run your organism properly, since you can be regarded as a fine instrument. This is much like learning to drive an automobile. Then you operate the devices near you on the dashboard and on the floor. We may call these devices the *controls*. If you are to learn to operate yourself properly, you must become able to observe your own controls and engineer them.

How You Operate Your Car

When you operate the controls of your car, your aim is to direct the wheels according to your desires and to make them go around slowly or fast or to stand still. This is driving. "The car moves because there is friction where the wheels turn on the ground. When we discuss your driving of yourself, we mean more than your locomotion and your other movements. Every performance of the automobile is movement over the ground, which depends on four wheels. However, not only do you move over the ground but you can move your arms and hands in countless different ways—and, also, other parts of your body. Besides this, you also have a moving picture camera and a second pictorial device as well, for you can see in imagination what is not actually present. Furthermore, you have a sound apparatus whereby you not only can hear but also can reproduce in imagination. Also, you have apparatus to smell and taste.

The Tissue Counterpart of Wheels

"In these and in other activities you have far more to operate than wheels, as in driving a car. Let us assume that, just as everything accomplished by the automobile in running is through operation of the wheels, so also all of your accomplishments in time and space are effected through the operation of one kind of tissue. Under this assumption, let us ask ourselves what tissue in our bodies serves the same purpose as the wheels?

Is it the skin? Evidently not, for this is chiefly a protective covering. Is it fat? No, fat is practically inert, and we are asking about something that moves. Is it the bones, since these move? No, these are merely pushed or pulled along. The blood moves; is it the blood? No, this is pushed along largely by the heart. What about connective tissue, which moves, contracts to form a scar, as in scar formation? Obviously, connective tissue does not take the place of wheels, for we could not move a hand or a foot by means of connective tissue.

"At this point you may say, 'I know, it is the brain that has to do with all our acts, as wheels have to do with all the movements of the automobile. I should have thought of this sooner!'

Brain Is Necessary But Not Sufficient

"No! Wrong again. We assume that, without a brain, we would not move. Children born anencephalic lie in a heap, helpless. But an automobile likewise is helpless if the motor is missing or out of order. We may liken the brain to what is under the hood of the car, namely, a chief portion of the necessary machinery. Certainly the nervous system, including the brain, must operate if you are to make any effort, but you do not change your environment, you do not act according to Newton's law of motion, you do not exert force on your surroundings directly by the soft tissues of your nervous system. Nerves are not your wheel-substitutes.

"The brain is commonly compared with 'central' of the telephone system. It is a good comparison, provided that the comparison is carried out fully. You cannot telephone without 'central.' But does 'central' do your telephoning? No! You do it! Without 'central,' you cannot telephone. 'Central' is necessary. Likewise, without a brain you cannot act. The brain is a necessary condition. But central is not sufficient by itself to telephone for you. You must use the phone at the periphery of the system. Likewise, your brain is necessary but not sufficient for forceful action, which depends on the tissue at the periphery of the system, namely, muscle.

How You Can Operate Your Organism

"Obviously, muscle occupies the place in your systematic actions which wheels occupy in the actions of automobiles. Muscle fibers shorten, which is called contraction and they lengthen, which is called relaxation. These actions compare with revolution of wheels. Since muscle fibers are of soft structure, they can take circuitous paths and, thus, when they shorten, produce very complicated movements of your organism and its parts.

"For the time being, we shall assume, on the basis of laboratory evidence, that everything you do mentally depends on at least minute shortening or lengthening of muscle fibers. Later on, you will have an opportunity to make certain observations on mental activity in yourself, and, to some extent, you may be able to form your own opinion based on your own observations.

"On the basis of these assumptions, everything you do all day long, whether so-called physical or mental, depends on muscle action. If this is true, then what you need to learn in order to control all your efforts is to operate your muscle-controls.

Learning To Recognize Your Efforts

"To learn more about the efforts you make in everything you do, I'll ask you to lie on your back during this first session. Please let your arms be at your sides and do not cross your legs. Also, let your eyelids remain open for several minutes, then close them gradually so that you will be prepared to observe some slight sensations. I shall try to show you what goes on when you perform work—make an effort—in any part of your body. You will need to observe closely, because the signal will be faint and you will miss it if you look for something strong, something that 'hits you hard.' I shall leave the room to let you get started at getting yourself as quiet as possible. Please keep your lids closed so that you can be prepared to notice carefully. You will have the opportunity to observe what goes on in any part of your body when you perform work there, that is, when you make any effort at all—whether housework or your efforts to avert blindness or the harm you are afraid you may do to someone. I want to teach you to recognize efforts, good ones as well as those which are bad for you in your estimation. Also, I want to teach you how to avoid efforts which do no good. Is that simple?"

"It sounds very simple."

"It is simple, but, also, it is direct. My job is not primarily to convince you of anything. It will be to try to show you how to observe and how to act. Do you dance?"

"I haven't danced much lately, but I love to dance."

The instructor, who had left the room, returned.

The Control Sensation Recognized

"Keeping your eyelids closed from now on, please bend back your left hand at the wrist. As you do so, see if you can observe a faint, diffuse sensation along here" (indicating the upper region of the left forearm; the patient nodded assent). "We will call this sensation or signal the control sensation or tenseness. It is *you* doing something, working, making an effort right there, as indicated by the sensation. You are to learn to recognize this kind of signal, whether faint or strong. You have been working like that and have been tense like that when you have made efforts not to be nervous and, also, when you have made efforts to avoid anxiety and fear in the attempt to gain security. I do not mean that, in these efforts, you always are tense in the same arm region and in the same way as now when you bend your left hand back at the wrist. The sensation of tension is the same, but the patterns of tension vary and may be anywhere else in the muscles of your body. During efforts to avert anxiety, the tension pattern generally will be all over, especially in muscles of the eyes and speech. These are matters which you will need to confirm for yourself and not accept on my say-so. But I have tried to give you a preview of what you are to learn to observe.

"Do you observe the sensation of tenseness now that you are bending the left hand back?"

"Yes."

Strain Recognized

"There is another sort of sensation in the wrist." (Indicating) "Please observe that it is not the same kind of signal as the one above it which we have called tenseness and which marks your effort. Let's call the different signal or sensation at the wrist *strain*. This is not *you doing* something, for, if I bend your hand back, the strain increases. It is something passive;

it is done to you. When you bend back your hand, you are doing something to your wrist, just as you might press something against your wrist and experience a sensation passively. However, the tenseness is different; it is *you* doing something actively.

"Let's go over the ground once more. Please bend back your left hand and notice again the sensation in the upper portion of your left forearm. We call this being tense, working *there*. It is you doing something. You have worked like that when you have made an effort not to be nervous. You work like that whenever you try to avoid some fear or achieve security. When you make any kind of effort, there is a tension pattern somewhere, composed of tensions which feel like the one you just performed. They are not limited to one particular region, such as the forearms, but often include many other regions, especially eye and speech muscles.

"Once more, notice the sensation of tenseness, of effort, of work performance on bending back your left hand. There it is, in the upper section of your left forearm." (Indicating.) "It is the same sensation of tenseness which you experience in another kind of pattern somewhere in your muscles when you make efforts to solve your difficulties. This includes efforts to protect yourself, to achieve security or to avoid harming people or going blind or committing suicide.

"Now, please bend your left arm at the elbow. You should notice the same kind of sensation as previously, but now it is in the biceps muscles, at the front of your upper arm." (Indicating.)*

Effort To Relax Is Failure To Relax

"Please discontinue bending, but make no effort to do so." (The patient followed the direction.) "That's good. You did a little work then, but you should not. Bend again and let go once more. That is still better. That is perfect.

---

* To save time in an abridged course, this patient was informed where she should look for the sensations of tension. In unabridged courses, the patient finds the sensation for himself. Often, this takes time.

"When you discontinue work in this manner, you are not working to relax. An effort to relax is not to relax.

(The patient was permitted to maintain the relaxation for several minutes while the instructor left the room. On his return, he requested her to make the entire left arm rigid without shift of position.)

"Hold it quiet! Stop moving it! Hold it stiff! That is the stopping of movement! Stopping like this is work. Likewise, stopping being nervous is work, if you do so by tensing your parts. That's not what we want, is it?" (The patient concurred.) "Now, please discontinue this effort to stop. That is good; you did not work to discontinue; you simply went negative. I will leave you for a time. While I am gone, please don't bother to do anything with your left arm; no effort, no work whatsoever."

(Returning, the instructor placed a book under the lower portion of the left forearm.)

Excessive Efforts for Comfort

"You made an effort, evidently, to get comfortable. To make unnecessary efforts to get comfortable is to be nervous. We are trying to teach you *not* to work to get comfortable, at least, not when you are practicing to relax. It is not that we plan to discard the goal of getting comfortable in life, but we are to discard your favorite method of trying to get comfortable by endless efforts. Of course, at times a little work performance can add to comfort. But let's correct your habitual tendency to make excessive efforts in order to get comfortable. You should overcorrect, if necessary, and do too little work for comfort rather than too much.

"Please press the left wrist down against the book and try to find the sensation of tension." (The patient pointed to the triceps region.) "Yes. That is *you* performing work there to fulfill my request. Please discontinue the effort of pressing." (She did this.) "That was well done." The patient continued to relax while the instructor left for several minutes.

Two Ways To Stop Motion

On his return, he stated: "During my absence, you maintained a relaxed state. You were not performing work and you were not moving your arm. However, it is possible for your arm to be motionless, yet making an effort. Please stiffen your whole arm and hold it rigid. You can do this, but not without effort. As you notice, your whole arm is tense, but it is motionless. You have discontinued moving it and are holding it quiet. As you see, there are two different ways to stop motion in a part. The first way is to relax, the second is to hold the part still.

Apply this lesson to the stopping of being nervous or fearful. You can try to stop being nervous or fearful by stiffening your muscles and, to some extent, you may succeed. But this is work. When you are nervous and fearful, you will find that you are tense in some part. You may try to stop being nervous by holding yourself more or less rigid or tense. This would be making an effort to stop being nervous. But making an effort to stop being fearful or nervous is piling up efforts on efforts. You are to learn to avoid making efforts to stop being fearful and nervous. Instead, you are to find any tension present when you are fearful or nervous and relax this directly. This requires no work performance. To relax is the opposite of work. It is ease itself.

"Let me repeat: a little while ago I put a book under your left wrist. Then you moved your arm to get comfortable. That was work; you tensed your arm. We are trying to teach you that there is a way to get comfortable without work. This is the way of relaxation. Nervous people habitually work to get comfortable. They pursue comfort like a Will o' the wisp. The more nervous they are, the more they make efforts for comfort and vice versa.

Nervousness Defined

"To be nervous may be defined as trying for comfort too hard and in too unorganized a manner. We are not discarding the goal of becoming comfortable, but we are discarding your method of getting that way, which is working to do it.

"There are times when a little work performance can add to comfort. But you overwork. Let's correct this and try to do too little work for comfort rather than too much.

"Please bend your right hand back at the wrist. Now, where is the work performance, the feeling of tension? Please point it out." (The patient did so correctly.) "You are right. There, you are working to fulfill my request. Tension is in the upper section of your right forearm. Please do not memorize the location of tension, because, when you are fearful or nervous, you do not know in advance where the pattern is going to be. You will need to find it at the time. Still better, you will need to keep yourself so relaxed that it does not begin at the time.

How People Become More Nervous

"Absence of effort is the easiest thing in the world, for it is only not to work. It is zero work. But the nervous person does not know this and he doesn't do things the easy way. *He does things the hard way.* He works to attain goals. What goals? In your case, to avert blindness, to avoid going insane. For these negative goals, you have been working with very good intentions. But you remember the old saying that good intentions pave the road to Hell.

"We are trying to teach you to avoid such intentions. For this reason, I shall not reassure you and tell you how much better you are or make other favorable comments. Reassurance is a step in the wrong direction. If I want to go to a particular place from here, I must walk in the right direction. No matter how much effort I made walking, if I walk in the wrong direction, I should never get there. That is why you have never gotten where you wanted to get. Efforts may accomplish a purpose, but, if they are in the wrong direction, they are bound to lead you astray.

Sacrifice Necessary

"When you make any effort, whatsoever it is, it is for a goal—a certain end. When you don't make that effort, you sacrifice that end. At least, you sacrifice the attainment of the goal by those means. You give up that road to the goal. That's a sacrifice of a kind. So, if you are not to be nervous, you will have to sacrifice something—give up something—give up the roads to security which you have used for 11 years."

"One bad habit I'll have to break is constantly looking for reassurance."

"That is one of the chief things you have to do. How fast can you do that this month?"

"I'm going to try hard—well, not too hard, just enough."

"You are not requested to 'co-operate.' You are going to school."

"You're the teacher and I'm the learner."

"It's your job entirely, not mine. But you have to follow instructions. And you have to practice, twice a day."

APRIL 28, 1956: INSTRUCTION PERIOD 2. (The patient reported that she had practiced on the arms at least once and, often, twice a day. She had gone out more than previously, but not always comfortably.)

"I am eating better. I don't have the nausea I had. When I get excited, I try to relax as far as I can at the moment. I did not realize until this last month that I often become tense and irritable with my children. Now I try to get their problems solved calmly, without my screaming at them. Does tension cause fear or vice versa?"

"Neither. There is no cause-and-effect relationship. Certain kinds of tension patterns are active in fear."

Controls Available: Differ From Automatic Controls

"In operating yourself as an instrument, you need to recognize the kind of controls which are available to you in your organism. On the wall is the electric light switch, and I shall ask you to step over to it and flip it on." (The patient did this.) "As you move the switch, the switch performs work. Your thumb, in moving it, likewise performs work. You may remember from your high school days that work is the application of a force over a distance. To some extent, up to this point, this is similar to your work-performance when you bend your hand back at the wrist. It is different insofar as there is no on-switch as there is in the case of the light, which goes on when the switch is moved properly. We wish now to turn the light off. Please do this." (The patient pushed the switch down and the light went off.) "Here you work with your thumb and the switch works in order to turn the light off.

This is by no means the same as when you wish to discontinue an effort, such as the one that is present when you bend your hand at the wrist. Please do so. Discontinue bending." (The patient followed the instructions.) "There was no work performance when you discontinued bending the left hand. This, then, is quite different from turning the light off. There is no such thing as a switch-off in the human organism such as that in this wall-switch. However, man sometimes makes controls of the same type as you employ when you discontinue an effort by relaxation. Here is an ice-water faucet and, if you press this little button, the water begins to pour. At this moment, if you make an effort, pressing the button in further, the water flows only more strongly. The only way to discontinue the flow of the ice-water is to cease your effort.

The only way to cease to bend your hand back is to discontinue your work performance. However, untaught persons generally make an effort to relax. On doing so, they fail to relax. They are trying to operate as if they had a switch like the one in this wall. This is wrong maneuver. All this ties in with what you have already learned about avoiding an effort to relax."

Instruction on April 28 was devoted also to controls of the musculature of the right leg, including progressive tension and relaxation of the entire limb.

Improvement Noted

MAY 27, 1956: INSTRUCTION PERIOD 3. The sitting posture was used from this date on.

The patient said that, since the last day of instruction, all four children had been home with the mumps.

"On some days it has been impossible to practice, but I don't think that I have lost any ground. When I practiced, I did very well. I tried to do the best I could. I was still on the watch for getting tied up and getting irritable and yelling.

"My husband says I am much better and I have gained 4 pounds. I was a premature twin and weighed only 2 pounds at birth. What about heredity?"

"If your parents are rabbits, what are you?"

"A rabbit."

"Some persons are born with tendencies to be more nervous than others. But you were not born anxious. If you had been born with one eye, this could not be corrected. Anxiety is an acquired characteristic."

"I must teach my daughter to relax when I get well."

JUNE 23, 1956: INSTRUCTION PERIOD 4. The patient reported that she had not been so successful this month. This was the first month in which she practiced in the sitting posture, and she found that she could not get the same relaxation as when lying. She believed that she should return to the lying posture. She sleeps and dreams all night. She felt a little more "on edge" this month. Her husband has been moody.

"I have to give in when he is moody if there is to be peace in the house. He is trying to give up smoking. Perhaps this is why I have not done so well this month."

"It is easy not to be emotional."

"I should just find the tensions."

Three Steps in Anxiety Control

"This is not enough. There are three steps which are of very great importance. The first step is to sit down and distinguish what you were concerned about, the issue, just as you distinguish between the road and the car which you drive. When you have become quite clear about this, *and not before*, then as a second step, do you find the controls, the effort tensions. Up to date you are not able to examine your entire body to find the tension-controls. You will have to confine yourself to the parts which have received practice, namely, the limbs.

But, at any rate, you can examine these parts for controls. While taking steps one and two, do not relax. Leave off the relaxing. Otherwise, you will be concerning yourself about a problem, thereby tensing, while at the same time you are trying to relax. This is wrong procedure. Only after you have completed step one and, subsequently, step two are you to go negative in the effort tensions which you have identified."

Further instruction on this date was concerned with putting power on and letting it go off in the musculature of the abdomen, the back and the respiration.

JULY 15, 1956: INSTRUCTION PERIOD 5. During the past 3 weeks the patient suffered from what her general practitioner called a virus infection. However, she practiced at least 1 hour a day.

"My husband and I are puzzled about the cause of my fears."

"If you are a housewife and find a room very dusty, your task is to clean it up."

"I understand this, but I do not understand how tension causes fears."

"Tensions do not cause fears, or vice versa. Tension patterns are what you are doing when you have what you call fears."

"My husband wants me to take a job, for he believes that this will help me."

"Your husband should be in charge of this clinic."

"I conceal knives so that I will not fear to harm somebody. Is this all right?"

"It is time now for you to omit this, giving yourself an opportunity to practice at the moment when fear arises."

"But I reflect all day as I work."

Differential Control

"Fears are one form of reflection. Irritability, your husband's kind of nervousness, is another. Your task when reflecting in any way is to learn to distinguish the problem (the road) from your tension state. Having made the distinction and having found the controls, you are to go off with the power you otherwise would be wasting. The nervous person does things the hard way. To bend your hand back at the wrist is hard. To go negative is easy. The nervous person prolongs his efforts to meet situations all day long and, perhaps, into the night. His efforts often are over-intense and disorganized. It is not necessary for you to be reflecting while you are washing dishes or clothes. Differential control is the skill we seek. However, this will involve experience with the eyes and speech, a stage which we have not yet reached."

Further Improvement

AUGUST 26, 1956: INSTRUCTION PERIOD 6.

"I have been fine, although I have not practiced for 2 weeks because of house guests. I managed to get in my practice lying down, but, when I am sitting, duties interfere. My husband states that I do not scream as I always used to. I am no longer disturbed when he is excitable as I used to be. I still get disturbed when I read something alarming, but not so much as I used to. I still have fears of high places and of boat rides. However, knives have not been bothering me. I have been using them freely. I have not had them on my mind at all."

Less Anxiety

SEPTEMBER 23, 1956: INSTRUCTION PERIOD 7.

"I have not been bothered much by fears, except that of blindness, suggested by an article which I read about a pilot who went blind from tension. My husband states that I will find things to worry about."

"You have *not* been directed to make up your mind not to worry. On the contrary, you have been instructed to distinguish between issue and tension state and, thereafter, to relax the tension state. We may assume that you tend to worry when you have high residual tension. This is, in a way, part of your effort to meet the world and solve your problems. It will not be necessary to relax all the tensions of the eyes which arise automatically in response to what you see. Our task is much less formidable than this, more like making a cake just sweet enough to be palatable."

Difference Between Tension and Strain

Instruction at this session concerned controls of forehead, brow and eyelid muscles. This was followed by moving a pen rhythmically in front of the patient, whereupon she reported tensions in the eyes in an effort to follow the pen. On closing the lids and imagining the pen, she reported eye-strain of effort to move the eyes. The difference between strain and tension was stated and illustrated.

"It is time that you made this distinction. Your failure at this moment indicates—in part, at least—why you have failed at home."

On being requested to imagine the pen moving slowly, then fast, then slowly once more, she reported "tension in the brain." Thereupon she was requested to go to the dresser and pick up a match-box, which she did.

"You used your brain to do this, but you do not need to concern yourself with it, since you cannot observe brain action. You picked up the matches with your hand. You can observe what took place in your hand and arm. In order to control your imagination, you do not bother about your brain. We are concerned with control of imagination."

Imagination

The patient was requested to imagine a skyrocket shooting up into the clouds; a bird flying from tree to tree; a bird standing still; a ball moving along the ground; the president of the United States; her own kitchen; her husband and her children. She reported tensions in the eyes. In order to save time in an abridged method she was reminded that eye tensions when performed voluntarily are to be called *controls*. Thereafter, as instructed, in place of reporting tensions in the eyes she stated, "I used my eye controls." On being requested to "imagine the pilot going blind," she reported that she employed her eye-controls to do this but, at the same time, became tense all over. She was informed that this illustrates that the eye-tensions are *key* or *trigger* tensions. The body became tense all over in response to the eye-tensions in seeing the pilot. Then she was requested to imagine some other matter of concern. And she reported use of the eye-controls to see in imagination knives with which she might hurt somebody.

"Why did you use these eye-controls? To oblige me here. But at home why do you?"

"Because I am afraid!"

"And therefore you make *efforts*. This is a new point, isn't it? You have always believed that the fears are forced on you."

"I am beginning to understand."

OCTOBER 21, 1956: INSTRUCTION PERIOD 8. The patient said that she and her children had had what were called virus infections and that this kept her from practicing the new procedures this month. Instead, she continued to practice the older procedures and requested repetition.

"I got up at night repeatedly to nurse the children but did not get back to sleep. I never have."

"You are giving yourself autosuggestions. Your task is to go off with the power regardless of the past. Properly done, this is easy. Your task by day is to run your organism in its best interests, including the interest of the family. This means that you are not continually making efforts regarding tomorrow but are permitting yourself to enjoy the present hour."

Used Eye Controls

Again, the pen was moved rhythmically back and forth from side to side before her open eyes.

"Report on what took place."

"I imagined the pen."

"Do you drive a car? If I asked you how you got to New Jersey would you answer, 'By the wheels turning?' If I put this light on (I turn the switch) do I do it by the light going on?"

"No!" (smiling) "By using the control!"

"You get the point, then?"

"Yes."

"Nervous people make a lot of trouble for themselves. Their intentions are good. They focus on goals without recognizing the energies which they expand. We're trying to teach you to count the costs and to run your organism by controls so that you make the most of the present.

NOVEMBER 18, 1956: INSTRUCTION PERIOD 9.

"My husband says that I am fine now; but he asks what is going to happen when I quit coming for instruction? He can't believe that I will continue to do so well. Now I enjoy my food whereas formerly I could not eat and had little appetite. My family doctor tells me that the instruction has done wonders for me. I have put on 10 pounds in weight, but I do not want to get fat. May I exercise?"

"Yes. You will receive a diet slip to keep your weight down."

Visual Imagery

In the sitting posture, the patient was requested to imagine a skyrocket shooting up into the clouds; a motorcar passing by quickly; a bird flying from tree to tree; a bird standing still; a ball rolling along the ground and the ball motionless on the ground. In all these instances she reported the use of eye-controls to see the matter mentioned in imagination. Then more personal matters were imagined, including the children, her husband, and the family doctor. Even in these personal matters she reported the use of eye controls.

DECEMBER 16, 1956: INSTRUCTION PERIOD 10. The patient reported that she had practiced regularly. Requested to recall her husband and then to recall quarreling with him, she reported the use of eye-controls plus tension all over. She was requested to recall the children, one after another and, subsequently, her husband's facial expression when he was irritated. In all these instances she reported the use of eye controls. She stated emphatically, "My eyes are my problem!"

Instructions on this day included observation of controls in closing and opening the jaws, smiling, pouting and pushing the tongue forward or retracting it. In most of these instances, the patient located the control-tension at once without aid.

Practice for Habitual Control

JANUARY 13, 1957: INSTRUCTION PERIOD 11. The patient had had a "cold" and a trying time during the previous 4 weeks, but had controlled herself very well. She had been giving her husband his own way and was finding it easier to get along. At times, however, "I don't want to give in and I fight that feeling."

"Relax it?"

"Yes. I feel that he is taking advantage."

"What about your fears?"

"Fears have come off and on this month, I have found the tensions and have relaxed them. They did not seem to haunt me. I could control them. I find that when I get upset they bother me more."

"Practice is needed to form a habit of control."

Instruction on this day related also to counting aloud to ten with diminishing tensions until the patient was instructed only to imagine that she was counting. Then she was requested to imagine that she was saying her name and address three times and, later on, the names of each of her children. In all of these instances, she generally reported the use of tongue, throat and chest controls. In addition, upon imagining counting, she reported the use of controls of the lips, the cheek and the abdominal muscles, as a rule.

Difficulties Center in Eyes and Speech Organs

FEBRUARY 10, 1957: INSTRUCTION PERIOD 12.

"I thought I lost a little ground this month. I tried to figure out why and decided I was not applying the methods enough when I am active. All my difficulty seems to lie in the eye and speech mechanism. My mind is active even when I relax my limbs. I find it difficult to discontinue thinking. I have been trying to find out why I am nervous and I find that I don't apply my lessons to my activity during my working hours."

"That is going to take a lot of practice."

"But at least now I know where the trouble is. I still have strain with my husband, as soon as any money-matter comes up. I try to let him have his own way, but I feel a strain even when I think about it. It may have been this feeling that brought back the nervousness. I let go but find that I can do it only for a few minutes at a time. The rest of my body is relaxed quite well. But this mental activity—I'm afraid that's going to be a problem with me."

"I think that you have been doing quite well."

"I didn't think I did."

Instruction in this period was devoted to further acts of imagination involving internal speech. She still reported in terms of tensions rather than of controls.

"You can sit next to the driver and watch him drive the motor-car, but this is not driving. If you do not put yourself in the driver's seat you're not going to accomplish what you have set out to do."

"During the last two weeks my fears returned, but I would not give in to them. I kept on about my business. I can locate the tension patterns more easily now."

MARCH 10, 1957: INSTRUCTION PERIOD 13. After the patient related details of her husband's attitudes, she was asked about her fears which she had failed to mention.

"I have not been interested in fears. I have not had fears; they have not bothered me. My husband has noticed a complete difference."

Instruction was continued on observation of what takes place during inner speech. Commonly, she reported the use of eye controls simultaneously with the speech controls.

Continued Improvement

APRIL 7, 1957: INSTRUCTION PERIOD 14.

"I feel well. I have changed my attitude toward my husband's irritability and that has made a big difference. Of course I get irritated sometimes, but I am conscious of it and, when I am conscious of it, I relax. I have learned to distinguish very clearly between what I am irritable about and how I feel toward him."

"Another way of saying it is that you distinguish the difference between your tension and what you are tense about."

"Yes. Lately, I find I can go to sleep like that!" (Snaps her fingers.) "I have practiced every day. If unpleasant thoughts occur, I relax. They don't stay with me as they used to."

Instruction on this date continued to concern acts of imagination concerning personal matters, such as saying something about the children or her husband. By the end of the period, she was told that she would probably be dismissed soon.

"I see that I have come quite a long way."

Follow-up

MAY 5, 1957. The patient came only to report. She stated that she had some fears when out shopping, but she did not give in and go home but relaxed instead until the fear passed.

Tension Pattern Distinguished From Issue

"I was upset because it did happen, because I had been feeling so good previously, perhaps too confident. I had a big argument with a dear friend, a neighbor, about her children and mine, and I felt bad about this. However, I distinguished between the issue and my tension attitude and in 2 or 3 days was no longer troubled. It is unusual for me to recover so quickly from such matters and I was very pleased. During the last 2 weeks I have practiced only 1 hour. Only now I am beginning to see how the technic works."

"What about fear of knives?"

"This does not bother me at all."

JUNE 30, 1957. The patient reported that she has practiced, although not every day, since the children have been at home. She had gained at least 25 pounds. Her husband had lost his position temporarily and they had no savings. However, she managed very well and her husband complimented her. She continued to be free from fears.

JULY 28, 1957. She continued to do very well.

AUGUST 25, 1957. She has done pretty well, although she had been obliged to nurse ailing children.

SEPTEMBER 22, 1957. The patient reported that she had been so occupied nursing the children that she had not been able to get a full night's sleep in 4 weeks . There had been no hour for practice. Occasionally, she practiced for a quarter of an hour. This did not seem to be enough. She had been in bed with the "flu" for 3 days. During the previous 2 weeks she practiced 2 hours a day but she did not seem to have got the technic. She reported that she was eating only with difficulty, slept only 3 hours and then felt sorry for herself and couldn't get back to sleep.

Refresher Instruction

Some instruction was given this hour in recalling her children all sick. This brought out that—as she expressed it—"I lose sight that I am doing it to myself. I'm speaking of tensions and meanings." However, she soon returned to reporting "I used my eye controls to picture the children."

NOVEMBER 17, 1957.

"I feel fine. There is no more 'flu.' I have reduced my weight and will try to keep it down. My husband is not well and fights, but I do not; I do not get excited any more. I finally got hold of myself when I wasn't doing well. I realize that when I was nervous it was myself doing and likewise when I couldn't sleep. It did not come from the outside. I was responsible. I kept reminding myself to put myself in the driver's seat. This has worked. There have been some fears but not to the point where they upset me. The thoughts come, but there is no emotion attached. I feel good and I sleep well."

Reports Discontinued

JUNE 12, 1960. The patient had been discharged and for several years I did not hear from her, assuming that she was getting along very well. However, on June 12, 1960 she phoned and said that she had been nervous and severely emotional.

Additional Responsibilities

After her discharge her husband had secured a position for her in the same concern in which he worked. In addition, she still had the responsibilities of taking care of her four children. This proved to be too much. She began to take sedatives every day, although she realized that this was contrary to the instructions she had received.

Returns to Tranquilizers

She consulted her family doctor without telling him of the instruction that she had received. Now she related that the doctor had prescribed Miltown and Deprol and has said to her, "Your trouble is only mental!" But when she failed to improve, he advised shock treatment or psychotherapy. Realizing that this advice implied a dependency, contrary to present principles, sobbing in despair, she cried, "I let you down!"

Severe Relapse

Thus, notwithstanding the brilliant results which had been attained and which persisted for 2 or 3 years, her husband's view that she would be aided by work proved to be unfortunate, leading to a series of tragic events. Unable to cope with her manifold duties to her children and her work, and contrary to instructions, she turned to the use of sedatives and tranquilizers. What was said by her family doctor in diagnosis, she stated, apparently proved shocking and led to more severe relapse.

Becomes Intractable

The patient came to the Chicago clinic for about 4 days, making a very rapid recovery. However, following her return to her home, relapse set in severely once more. On a second visit to Chicago her husband found her one morning beginning to slit her throat with a razor blade. Thereafter she was depressed. She showed signs of very marked spasm of the esophagus with great difficulty in eating. It was necessary at this stage to prescribe medication such as Deprol, since she failed to respond satisfactorily to instructions. Due to the distance between her home and the Chicago clinic, treatment was terminated unsatisfactorily. From a young, ambitious woman, vital, energetic and handsome as she appeared when she was dismissed from instruction in 1957, she had become an aging, decrepit woman.

Importance of Continued Supervision

The lesson to be learned by the doctor from this study is the wisdom and the necessity of keeping regularly in touch with the patient after discharge, whether using present methods of instruction or any other procedures. Otherwise, the patient's emotional welfare is placed under the possible influence of other members of the family, who often consider themselves authorities on such matters. Likewise, especially after abridged forms of instructive treatment, careful supervision is imperative. This can be done by various means, including regular personal reports by phone or by letter if not in person. With these precautions in mind let us turn to the following case, in which they were carried out.

CASE 2. PHOBIC ANXIETY

As will be seen, the instructions are based on physiologic principles without underlying ideology.* The results follow promptly, as contrasted with the delays and the years of treatment by psychoanalysis often accorded to conditions of the same type. However, such favorable results should not be expected unless the doctor is willing to devote the same amount of energy to learning the skills of tension control methods as he would to other specialized fields of medicine. Then he will know why and how to avoid the use of suggestive and auto-suggestive therapy. Thus the doctor will build upon rock and will not be likened unto a foolish man which built his house upon the sands . . . and great was the fall of it.†

Complaints and History

The patient—a laboratory technician, 28 years of age, Negro, female, married, with one child—was first seen on August 22,

* Bailey, P., A. J. Psych., 113, 5, 397, 1956
† St. Matthew, Chap. VII. 26, 27.

1959. She complained of nervousness, anxiety, a general slight feeling of tremor, and dizziness on lying and arising. She was afraid to use the subway and to travel by herself.

She said that she had been married in 1953 and had been beset by marital problems. Her husband lacked ambition; he wanted to go to school and become an engineer but did not want to do the necessary work. She described him as an intelligent man, 30 years of age, of nervous disposition, able to get along, a very good father to their 4-year-old boy, but "easy" in his disposition of money (e.g., instead of paying the rent, he buys something else). Even though he was an irresponsible man, she stated that they loved each other. In 1958 she had sought advice from a marriage counselor.

Onset and Course

In 1954 she became pregnant for the first time. Previously, she used a diaphragm to avoid pregnancy. She was somewhat nervous during pregnancy and was given phenobarbital by her physician. Nervousness in the subway first appeared in the summer of 1955 following childbirth in March. Thereafter she sometimes forced herself to take the subway but usually took the elevated road instead. In June of that same year she became very ill while working and feared to take the train. Soon she became fearful even on going to work and had to force herself to go on some days. After keeping this up for about 2 weeks, she secured a leave of 6 weeks. She returned to work for 2 weeks but quit for good in September 1955. After she stopped working she stayed at home, afraid to go out to shop or to go into the street. Gradually, she got better, with the aid of a book on self help.

Psychoanalysis

In October 1956 she consulted a psychologist who told her that she was "afraid of sex."

"He said that I felt guilty unconsciously. I saw him once a week for 6 months. He gave me Thorazine which I took for 2 weeks. Fever set in and he told me to stop. I wanted to continue with him, but I had no money. I had no sex trouble that I knew of. But after he told me that I gradually got better. I was able to walk a block and even to take a bus. Not till July 1959 did I return to work. I take two buses to the subway, but sometimes my husband drives me or even I drive myself. I will not go on the subway alone, but I will go with him. I will go on the Long Island Railway alone."

Family History

Born in New York, she had gone to public school and had finished in 1949, after which she attended a school of laboratory training for 2 years and then went to college for one semester. She had been a nervous child. Her father was irritable, of fighting disposition and often drank. Both her sleep and her play suffered. At night she and her sisters feared that he would go on a rampage and hit their mother. They did not discuss the matter but hid their feelings.

She lived at home till she was 20 years old.

Her mother died at the age of 61 with high blood pressure. Her father was living but suffered from diabetes at the age of 63. One brother was severely nervous and another brother suffered from paranoid schizophrenia and was in the Veterans Hospital. A third brother, 20 years old, was nervous. She had four sisters. The eldest, aged 40, was nervous and irritable. Two of the others were "impulsive." The second sister was impulsive, but quiet and withdrawn. She was a nurse, shy, with few friends. Another sister, 19 years of age, was ill tempered, irritable and nervous and the youngest sister, 17 years of age, likewise was nervous.

Her previous maladies included varicella and pertussis in childhood.

Her menstrual history was negative.

She smoked a half package of cigarettes per day, drank two cups of tea, but avoided coffee. She seldom drank alcohol.

Examination

General examination disclosed a strongly built, handsome

woman about 5 feet 7 inches in height, weighing about 150 pounds. There were no marked evidences of pathology.

Course of Instruction, Self-Operations Control

AUGUST 22, 1959: INSTRUCTION PERIOD 1. Instruction was begun on self-operations control, in the lying posture.

"You are here to learn to operate yourself effectively as an instrument in your own interest. I have said that the responsibility is completely yours. I promise nothing. I guarantee nothing. I will try to teach you."

In the sitting posture the patient was requested to bend back the left hand at the wrist and to notice the sensation in the upper section of the forearm. It was agreed to call this the "control sensation."

"Relaxation will be the disappearance of the control sensation. This is no work performance. Effort to relax is failure to relax. Effort to overcome fears likewise is tension. The task of relaxing fears is the task of relaxing tension patterns, which is easy, since no effort is required."

During the first period, instruction was devoted to the neuromuscular controls of the left arm. Instruction included progressive tension and relaxation of the left arm. No instruction was given on the right arm.

SEPTEMBER 19, 1959: INSTRUCTION PERIOD 2. Dizziness had been present for 3 months, but now has been absent during the last 4 weeks. The patient's blood pressure was 108/70.

Instruction was devoted to recognizing the controls from the chief muscle groups of the left leg and going off with the power in each region. This was in the lying posture.

Fears Subside

OCTOBER 17, 1959: INSTRUCTION PERIOD 3. The patient reported that she rode in the subway on three different occasions during the month without fears. "But morning nausea has troubled me, although I am not pregnant."

Instruction in this session concerned the control patterns in the right leg, the abdomen and the back. As the patient went off with the power on three different occasions in the instance of the right foot extension she exerted marked contraction of the antagonists. This was corrected.

DECEMBER 12, 1959: INSTRUCTION PERIOD 4. The patient said that she had had no phobias, except a little when she was fatigued.

I pointed out that as she presently experiences fear she gives evidence of holding her breath. Her task is to relax tension patterns at the moment of fear.

Instruction concerned the controls of breathing, the pectoral groups, the muscles which elevate the shoulders and those which pull them back.

Uses Subway

JANUARY 9, 1960: INSTRUCTION PERIOD 5. The patient reported gleefully that now she was able to ride in the subways with her husband without fears.

"I am working!" she exclaimed gleefully. "That's something. Otherwise, I might not be."

Instruction concerned bending the head in various directions. On bending to the left and being requested to go off with the power the patient replaced her head three times and this error was called to her attention.

FEBRUARY 6, 1960: INSTRUCTION PERIOD 6. As yet the patient had not gone alone in the subway. Instruction was devoted to the muscles of the forehead, the brow, the eyelids and the eyes, looking in various directions as well as looking straight forward.

Relapse

MARCH 5, 1960: INSTRUCTION PERIOD 7. The patient reported a relapse.

"I have not felt so good, but I have not practiced because I was sick. They want to remove my tonsils. I have fears of this. I have missed practice for 2 weeks and feel bad because of missing it. I feel better when I practice each day. It seems that I'll have to practice the rest of my life. I am still riding on the subway with my husband, which I would not have done before. I still am going to work daily which I could not do previous to instruction. Now I am able to stay home alone and feel all right, which I did not before. Sometimes in the morning I awaken and have sleep paralysis and then I can't get up. I go negative and then I can relax myself out of it."

"You are giving yourself an autosuggestion. This is not at all necessary."

APRIL 2, 1960: INSTRUCTION PERIOD 8. Instruction for the first time was in the sitting posture. After leaving the patient alone with her head in drooping position, I returned to find her holding her head up and asked why.

"I was trying to find out how I'd be most comfortable."

"The nervous person makes efforts for comfort. Accordingly, you go into the subway and require your husband for comfort. Is this clear?"

"Yes."

In the sitting posture, instruction was given concerning the patterns in moving the head back, forward, left and right.

"Do not tense for good reasons while I am out of the room. Certainly do not tense for bad reasons. Is that clear?"

"Yes."

Toward the end of the hour the patient was requested to hold her head up while going negative in the neck muscles so far as possible in this posture. She had difficulty at first in that she held her head partially backward, but, later this was corrected.

Application of Control to Phobias

APRIL 30, 1960: INSTRUCTION PERIOD 9. The patient reported definite improvement.

"I am better. I feel fine. I go into the subway with my husband and my next step will be to go without him. I improve by steps."

In the sitting posture, instruction was devoted to the regions of the forehead, the brows and the eyelids. While wrinkling her forehead, slightly frowning and winking, the patient was requested to illustrate what she should do with these patterns of hers during a phobia. Promptly, she went negative.

Relapse With Neglect of Practice

MAY 28, 1960: INSTRUCTION PERIOD 10. The patient had had coryza for about two months and had been coughing. Nevertheless, she had remained at work, with the exception of 2 days. Roentgenograms of the chest were negative, but a diagnosis had been made of streptococcus sore throat. She had been taking antibiotics. She reported that her nervous condition had been "pretty good" but she has to practice.

"If I go 2 or 3 days without practice, I become nervous again. As yet, I have not had time to try to go to the subway alone."

Instruction in this period concerned patterns of the eye regions *with open eyes*. The patient was requested to look up, down, right, left and straight forward; in all these instances she reported that she observed the effort-tensions. Thereafter, a pen was moved rhythmically back and forth in front of her open eyes; she reported control patterns in following the pen. Requested to close her eyes and to imagine the pen moving back and forth before her at the same rate and in the same manner as previously when her eyes were open, she reported that she had eye tensions to the right and to the left rhythmically. Thereupon, she was requested to make the imagined pen go very slowly, then to go fast, and later, to go slowly again. Asked if she had done so, she replied affirmatively.

"How? How did you make the pen go back and forth at the various rates you desired?"

"I used my eyes."

"If you relax your eyes, what happens?"

"The imagination does not occur."

In succession, with intervals to relax the eyes, she was requested to imagine a skyrocket shooting up in the sky, a bird flying, the bird standing still, and the President of the United States. In all of these instances, she reported the use of eye controls.

"I had fear of going out by myself but overcame this myself. Then I had fear of work and I have relaxed for this. My worst fear concerns the subway."

Visual Imagination

JUNE 25, 1960: INSTRUCTION PERIOD 11. The patient was requested to imagine a man walking by; her hat on the table; a blade of grass; and the subway. In all instances, she reported the use of eye controls.

"Imagine being in the subway in a panic."

"I noticed eye tension. And a slight feeling of panic elsewhere."

After a few minutes devoted to going negative, she was requested to imagine the same once more. She reported that the emotional experience became less marked.

JULY 23, 1960: INSTRUCTION PERIOD 12. The patient reported that, unexpectedly, she had had a 4- to 6-weeks abortion. She had not known that she was pregnant, but went to be examined for a suspected cyst. In the operating room she became frightened but began to relax and soon went under the anesthetic. Since then, she had had no opportunity to go on the subway alone but had been free from phobias.

"Nothing bothers me much. I slept well at the hospital. I was home for 7 to 10 days and slept much of the day. I did not practice. I am still tired after the operation. In going with someone else in the subway, I practiced relaxing my eyes and my trunk. This made me feel better."

Instruction in this period concerned patterns in the musculature of the jaw, the cheek, the lip and the tongue. The patient was requested to observe what takes place during counting. Her reports were anatomically correct except that she omitted to mention chest tension in counting until this was brought to her attention.

AUGUST 20, 1960: INSTRUCTION PERIOD 13.

"This month I have been too busy to practice. I have been busy in the laboratory and we have had emergencies. My husband also has been very busy and often does not get home until 7 P.M. In the morning he often leaves at 6:30 A.M. I have to tend to the child in the morning and to get him off to nursery school at 8 A.M.

"I have had no time to have phobias so I just think about them. I have had no opportunity to go into the subway alone and I do not believe I would faint as I formerly would."

Instruction concerned tension patterns in speech and in verbal imagination.

Acrophobia Absent

SEPTEMBER 17, 1960: INSTRUCTION PERIOD 14.

"I no longer have any fears like those of heights. I just look out of the window without trouble. At first, when I began, I felt that the instruction was not doing me any good, but, later, I found that I had to practice and that, if I didn't for 2 or 3 weeks, I noticed the difference."

The patient proposed to take half-way measures at first, going alone to the subway but having her husband meet her.

Further instruction included acts of imagination concerning personal matters, such as her purse and her husband.

Discharge and Follow-up

The patient was discharged, but, learning from the case reported in the first portion of this chapter, I requested her to report every 4 weeks.

OCTOBER 15, 1960. The patient stated that she has been able to go to sleep alone in the apartment since her husband was taken to the hospital with a blood clot in his ankle.

"I am confident that I could go into the subway alone, since I can sleep alone. I have been very tense with many duties because of my husband's illness."

No Phobic Experiences

NOVEMBER 12, 1960. The patient reported progress.

"I am doing fine. Once I went into the subway alone. As soon as my husband has recovered, I will go more often. I have slept peacefully in the apartment alone. This has never been possible for me before. As I have become more relaxed I put on weight. I have put on 12 pounds."

She was given a diet reduction slip. She said that during the past 5 years, following her pregnancy, she had gained a total of 60 pounds. She was practicing 5 to 6 days per week, usually one hour, following her work. She was greatly pleased over her recovery and no longer took tranquilizers.

"I took tranquilizers before I came and they made me worse. At first I used Thorazine. I do not recall what I took last. I felt better after I stopped taking these tranquilizers."

"Do you have any other fears?"

"No disturbing fears. I get along better on the job. Formerly, I forced myself to go to work and I was fearful to go out alone. Now I drive my own car every day. I no longer am fearful when I get on the bus. Previously I could not get on the bus without fear. Now it has become mere routine."

Fatigue Diminished

DECEMBER 10, 1960.

"My husband's sister died after her husband had been injured by a motorcar. I have had much extra work to do in consequence and am tired. I find practicing a *must*. My fatigue is diminished. I follow the cards and will continue to do so."

Daily Practice Necessary

JANUARY 7, 1961. The patient reported, "I am doing pretty well. I keep up my practice, else I don't feel good. I can't get along without that."

She had been practicing in the lying posture on the trunk. This month she will practice on the neck and the eye regions.

"I have no fears as long as I practice. Fears don't bother you if you practice. I have had no opportunity to go to the subway, but my husband finds that I get along even better without him."

FEBRUARY 4, 1961. The patient's report was satisfactory.

I feel fine. I have had no opportunity to go into the subway alone."

MARCH 3, 1961. The patient admitted failure to practice regularly.

"I have been feeling pretty well but I have practiced only 17 out of 28 days. I have gone into the subway a short distance alone without fear. I plan to go home today by subway. I don't think much about my fears; they are not so important any more."

"That's why you're not practicing; but this is a mistake!"

APRIL 29, 1961. The patient stated that she was in excellent condition and that she goes into subways if need be, but had little occasion to do so.

MAY 26, 1961. The patient said that she was practicing and was doing very well indeed. She was eating less.

Abridged Course Saves Time

This case is recorded as an instance of an abridged course which has met with positive therapeutic results. These results have been safeguarded by having the patient report regularly with a view to seeing that she continues to practice. We should emphasize that the value of abridged courses rests in a saving of the doctor's time.

Longer Courses Provide More Thorough Education

However, to save time of the instructor is not under all conditions the most important consideration. Even if a result can be achieved successfully, and the instructor saves time, it is obvious that a prolonged course of instruction in this field is as significant as would be the case in any other field of education.

For the Doctor With Little Time (or Much)

However pressed for time, the doctor cannot escape the obligation to help his tense patients. It is often estimated that more than half of the patients seen by the average doctor are overtense and that their symptoms are either exaggerated or wholly a consequence of the tension. Such estimates concerning their own practices recently have been communicated to the author by a noted orthopedist and a noted surgeon, both of Chicago. According to the former, "Many of my patients with complaints of arthritis are examples. To have minor joint troubles from time to time can be expected, for scarcely anyone is lastingly trouble-free. However, these complaining patients, without knowing it, really come to my clinic because of their tensions."

For use with the many tense patients in every doctor's field, the directions for tension control practice in Chapter 6 are reproduced in pamphlet form. It is suggested that the doctor indicate to his patients how to follow the directions and practices therein outlined.

In this, even a very brief time of explanation and personal instruction by the doctor may prove of help. As little as an hour or two of personal instruction is advocated, if no more time can be expended. "Half a loaf is better than none!" The results thus secured will not be proved, for control tests will be lacking. However, even brief instruction often is considered helpful by the patients themselves. For example, a noted statesman, conspicuously anxious and overemotional in his speeches and other executive duties, learned enough in about 3 hours to correct the disturbance. In follow-up 9 years later, those close to him reported that the correction had proved lasting.

For the doctor with sufficient time, the pamphlet instructions can be employed for daily directions and for practice. If he learns self-operations control himself, so much the better!

Tension Measured in Action Potentials

Tension Control is an engineering science based on action-potential measurements. When we speak of effort patterns or neuromuscular patterns, we are not speculating, for these patterns are precisely what we see on the oscilloscope screen, what we photograph and what we measure.

Measurements on this order have been conducted approximately daily in our Laboratory for Clinical Physiology since 1936. Previously, they were conducted in the Physiological Laboratory of the University of Chicago. The earliest measurements had to be conducted in the Dunes of Indiana until I had rendered the apparatus sufficiently free from induction to employ it on the campus.

In these efforts I had the benevolent cooperation of the Bell Telephone Laboratories, thanks to the generous contribution as a public service made by their leaders, successively Research Director Arnold, President Oliver Buckley and President Mervin Kelley. Thanks are due also to Engineers Halsey S. Frederick and David G. Blattner.

When in 1927 I began with the aid of the earliest of these most distinguished associates, they doubted the possibility of achieving the measurement of the low voltage transients in which I was interested. While I conceded that it might prove impossible, I had secured sufficient experience in the electronics of that day to feel warranted in going ahead and they kindly agreed. In the end, success was attained. By 1930 I was

202

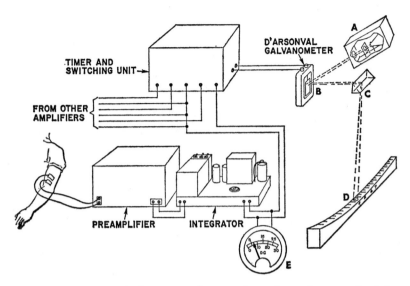

Fig. 7. A pair of platinum iridium surface electrodes over the left biceps-brachial muscles (3 other pairs simultaneously in 3 other selected regions are not illustrated). Potential differences in the electrodes vary with the degree of contraction—phasic or steady—in the selected muscle group. These voltages are amplified and rectified and then charge a condenser. Every 2 minutes this charge is measured as follows: The condenser is discharged by means of a timer and switching unit periodically through a d'Arsonval galvanometer with an attached mirror (B). Light from a source (A) is reflected first to this mirror and then to a prism (C) and then to a scale (D). Thus, a spot of light moves on the scale and returns to zero. The extent of this movement is standardized with a calibrating unit in terms of microvolts. Using a slide rule, the technician records the averaged microvoltage for each muscle group at the end of every 2-minute interval of the test. The fluctuations of neuromuscular tension in each muscle group are indicated on a meter (E) continuously. There is a meter in each circuit. In the testing of a tense or emotional person the indicators may be observed to fluctuate and remain at high values. In a patient adequately trained in relaxation such fluctuations are diminished or largely absent. The indicator remains at or near zero for most or all of the test.

measuring the transients in questions successfully. Ever since then from time to time I have improved the apparatus, increasing the stability and reducing the noise-to-signal ratio. We presently measure action-potentials in microvolts, which is

1000th of a millivolt, the unit employed in electrocardiography. (See Fig. 7.) Commercial electromyographic and electro-encephalographic equipment generally does not have the necessary voltage sensitivity with stability to be employed for present purposes.

To measure mental activity was among the first objectives. Accordingly, subjects trained to relax were requested to engage in simple acts of imagination. The findings offered convincing evidence (1) that mental activities involve the neuromuscula-ture and (2) that they can be measured in this peripheral structure showing action potential patterns simultaneous with and obviously corresponding in pattern with the character of the mental activity. (Interested readers will find accounts thereof in the bibliographic references at the end of this volume, as well as references from other laboratories confirm-ing my results.) These studies showed also that, if the neuro-muscular patterns were absent, the mental activity in question was absent. If the subject relaxed the specific patterns or they were absent for any other reason, no corresponding mental activity took place.

I shall not give here a detailed account of apparatus or of successive developments, since this has been done elsewhere. The integrating neurovoltmeter is used to secure action-potential performance in patients at times before, during and toward the termination of instruction or thereafter. The results are instructive.

While action-potential studies have an extremely important role in these and other respects to support a basic science, we should not rely upon them exclusively any more than the cardiologist or the internist in any field should rely on lab-oratory findings alone.

As a guide to judging therapeutic results, there are appar-ently four lines of evidence.

1. The evidence from the patient's account, symptom by symptom, progress or retrogression, bearing in mind that this account may be erroneous in either respect;

2. The evidence from

A. Repeated physical and clinical laboratory examinations, if indicated for repetition in test

B. The physician's observation of the behavior of the patient and his clinical appearance;

3. The patient's output in work or other occupation;

4. Graphs of action potential measurements.

The case histories related in previous chapters will present sufficient evidence to enable the reader to estimate the apparent therapeutic results without the aid of the graphs. In the interest of brevity and simplicity, I shall omit description of the graphs from the patients mentioned. In the present instances, I find the graphic data too highly complicated for condensed analysis. Moreover, some of the patients were not available for measurement; others failed to show improvement or retrogression or relapse *pari passu* with clinical findings thereof.

With any patient, therapeutic achievements can be evaluated satisfactorily if all of the four criteria stated above are satisfied. At best, the patient under direction eventually reduces his tension action potentials approximately to zero level. When this is accomplished in performance tests to include eyes and speech, we rate the patient as expert and we find that daily practice can keep him so with results that prove lasting.

Bibliography

Anxiety

Dickel, H. A.: Inherent dangers in use of tranquilizing drugs in anxiety states, J.A.M.A., *163:*422-426, 1957.

Dixon, H. H., Dickel, H. A., Shanklin, J. G., Peterson, R. D., and West, E. S.: Therapy of anxiety states and anxiety complicated by depression, Western J. Surg. *62:*338-341, 1954.

Fiorica, V., and Muehler, S.: Relationship between plasma levels of 17-hydroxycorticosteroids (17-OH-CS) and a psychological measurement of manifest anxiety, Psychosomatic Medicine November-December, p. 596, 1962.

Freud, S.: The Problem of Anxiety, H. A. Bunker, (Trans.) Psychoanal. Quart. p. 91-92, 1936.

Haugen, G. B., Dixon, H. H., and Dickel, H. A.: A Therapy for Anxiety Tension Reactions, N. Y., Macmillan, 1958.

Jeans, R. F., and Toman, J. E. P.: Anxiety and cerebral excitability, Arch. Neurol., *75:*534, 1956.

Leavitt, E. E., and Persky, H.: Anxiety, Psychosomatic Medicine p. 218, 1960.

Persky, H., Maroc, J., Conrad, E., and Den Breyen, A.: Anxiety, Psychosomatic Medicine. September-October, p. 379, 1959.

Emotion

Brady, Joseph: Neurophysiology, Chap. 63, p. 1529, American Physiological Society, 1960.

Cohen, R.: The influence of emotion on the human electroencephalogram, J. Nerv. Ment. Dis. *104:*351-357, 1946.

Chapman, W. P., Schroeder, H. R., Geyer, G., Brazier, M., Fager, C., Poppin, J. L., Solomon, H. C., and Yakovlev, P. J.: Physiological evidence concerning importance of the amygdaloid nuclear region in the integration of circulatory function and emotion in man, Science *120:* 949-950, 1954.

Darrow, C. W.: Emotion as relative function decortication: The role of conflict, Psychol. Rev. *42:*566-578, 1935.

Gellhorn, Ernst, and Loofbourow, G. N.: Emotions and Emotional Disorders, N. Y., Harper & Row, 1963.

Gellhorn, Ernst: Physiological Foundations of Neurology and Psychiatry, Univ. Minnesota Press, 1953.

Kraines, S. H.: Emotions: A physiologic process, Psychosomatics, November-December, p. 313, 1963.

207

Rapaport, David: Emotions and Memory, New York, Internat. Univ. Press, 1950.

Simon, Alexander; Herbert, Charles; and Straus, Ruth: The Physiology of Emotions, Springfield, Ill., Thomas, 1961.

Electrical Measurement of Nervous and Muscular States

Jacobson, Edmund: The direct measurement of nervous and muscular states with the integrating neurovoltmeter (action-potential integrator), Am. J. Psychiat. 97:513-523, 1940.

————: Differential relaxation during reading, writing, and other activities as tested by the knee-jerk, Am. J. Physiol. 86:675-693, 1928.

————: Measurement of the action-potentials in the peripheral nerves of man without anesthetic, Proc. Soc. Biol. Med. 30:713-715, 1933.

————: Electrical measurements concerning muscular contractions (tonus) and the cultivation of relaxation in man—studies on arm flexors, Am. J. Physiol. 107:230-248, 1934.

————: Electrical measurements concerning muscular contractions (tonus) and the cultivation of relaxation in man—relaxation times of individuals, Am. J., Physiol. 108:573-580, 1934.

————: The Neurovoltmeter, Am. J. Psychol. 52:620-624, 1939.

————:An integrating voltmeter for the study of nerve and muscle potentials, Rev. Scient. Instruments, 11:415-418, 1940.

————: The effect of daily rest without training to relax on muscular tonus, Am. J. Psychol. 55:248-254, 1942.

————: Les principes soulignant les méthodes de la relaxation, Revue scientifiques de médecine psychosomatiques 3:49-56, 1961.

Electrical Measurement of Mental Activities:
Anxiety; Other Emotions; Dreams

Aserinsky, E., and Kleitman, N.: Eye movements during sleep, Fed. Proc. 12:13, 1953.

————: Two types of ocular motility occurring in sleep, J. Appl. Physiol. 8:1-18, 1955.

————: A motility cycle in sleeping infants as manifested by ocular and gross bodily activity, J. Appl. Physiol. 8:11-18, 1955.

————: Regularly occurring periods of eye motility and concomitant phenomena, during sleep, Science 118:273-274, 1953.

Berger, R.: Tonus of extrinsic laryngeal muscles during sleep and dreaming, Science 134:840, 1961.

Courts, F. A.: Relations between muscular tension and performance, Psychiat. Bull. 39:347-367, 1942.

Davis, R. C.: Patterns of muscular activity during "mental" work and their constancy, J. Exp. Psychol. 24:451-465, 1939.

Dement, W.: "Dream recall and eye movements during sleep in schizophrenics and normals, J. Nerv. Ment. Dis. 122:263, 1955.

Dement, W., and Kleitman, N., Cyclic variations in EEG during sleep and their relation to eye movements, body motility and dreaming, Electroenceph. Clin. Neurophysiol. 9:673-690, 1957.

Dement, W., and Kleitman, N.: The relation of eye movements during sleep to dream activity: an objective method for the study of dreaming, J. Exp. Psychol. 53:339-346, 1957.

Dement, W., and Wolpert, E. A.: The relation of eye movements, body motility, and external stimuli to dream content, J. Exp. Psychol. 55:543, 1958.

Freeman, G. L.: Mental activity and the muscular processes, Psychol. Rev. 38:428-449, 1931.

Gould, L. N.: Verbal hallucinations and activity of vocal musculature, an electromyographic study, Am. J. Psychiat. 105:367-372, 1948.

Jacobson, Edmund: Action currents from muscular contractions during conscious processes, Science 66:403, 1927.

————: Imagination of movement involving skeletal muscle, Am. J. Physiol. 91:567-608, 1930.

————: Imagination and recollection of various muscular acts, Am. J. Physiol, 94:22-34, 1930.

————: Visual imagination and recollection, Am. J. Physiol. 95:694-702, 1930.

————: Evidence of contraction of specific muscles during imagination, Am. J. Physiol. 95:703-712, 1930.

————: Variation of specific muscles contracting during imagination, Am. J. Physiol. 96:115-121, 1931.

————: A note on mental activities concerning an amputated limb, Am. J. Physiol. 96:122-125, 1931.

————: Imagination, recollection and abstract thinking involving the speech musculature, Am. J. Physiol. 97:200-209, 1931.

————: Electrophysiology of mental activities, Am. J. Psychol. 44:677-694, 1932.

————: Electrical Measurement of Activities in Nerve and Muscle in the Problem of Mental Disorder, pp. 133-145, N. Y., McGraw-Hill, 1934.

————: You Can Sleep Well, 144, ff. N. Y., McGraw-Hill, 1938.

————: Electrical measurements of mental activities in man, Trans. N. Y. Acad. Sci. 2:272-273, 1946.

Lorens, S. A., Jr., and Darrow, C. W.: Eye movements, EEG, GSR and EKG during mental multiplication, Electroenceph. Clin. Neurophysiol. 14:739-746, 1962.

Max, L. W.: An experimental study of the motor theory of consciousness 3. Action current responses in deaf mutes during sleep, sensory stimulation and dreams, J. Comp. Psychol. 19:469-486, 1935.

————: An experimental study of the motor theory of consciousness. 1. Critique of earlier studies, J. Gen. Psychol. 11:112-125, 1934.

————: An experimental study of the motor theory of consciousness. 4. Action-current responses in the deaf during awakening, kinesthetic imagery and abstract thinking, J. Comp. Psychol. 24:301-344, 1937.

————: Action current responses in deaf mutes during sleep, sensory stimulation and dreams, J. Comp. Psychol. 19:469-486, 1935.

Roffwarg, H. P., et al.: Dream imagery: Relationship to rapid eye movements of sleep, Arch. Gen. Psychiat. 7:27-50, 1962.

Schiff, S. K., Bunney, W. E., Jr., and Freedman, D. X.: A study of ocular movements in hypnotically induced dreams, J. Nerv. Ment. Dis. 133:59-68, 1961.

Shaw, W. A.: Relation of muscular action potentials to imaginal weight lifting, Arch. Psychol. 35:1940, 50 pp.

————: The distribution of muscular action-potentials during imagining, Psychol. Record, 1938.

Snyder, Frederick: The new biology of dreaming, Arch. Gen. Psychiat. 8:381-391, 1963.

Wolpert, E. A.: Studies in the psychophysiology of dreams. 2. An electromyographic study of dreaming, Arch. Gen. Psychiat. 2:231, 1960.

General

Bailey, Percival: The Academic Lecture, Am. J. Psychiat. 113:387-406 1956.

Freeman, G. L.: Spread of neuromuscular activity during mental work, J. Gen. Psychol. 5:479-494, 1931.

Jacobson, Edmund: On meaning and understanding, Am. J. Psychol. 22:553-577, 1911.

————: The use of relaxation in hypertensive states, N. Y. Med. J., March 1920.

————: The reduction of nervous irritability and excitement by progressive relaxation, Trans. Soc. Nerv. Ment. Dis. A.M.A., 1920.

————: Progressive relaxation, Am. J. Psychol. 36:73-87, 1925.

————: Voluntary relaxation of the esophagus, Am. J. Physiol. 72:387-394, 1925.

————: Response to a sudden unexpected stimulus, J. Exp. Psychol. 9:19-25, 1926.

————: Spastic esophagus and mucous colitis, Arch. Int. Med. 39:433-435, 1927.

————: Progressive Relaxation, Univ. Chicago Press, May, 1929; Rev. Ed., U. of Chicago Press, 1938.

————: The physiological conception and treatment of certain common psychoneuroses, Am. J. Psychiat. 98:219-226, 1941.

————: The effect of daily rest without training to relax on muscular tonus, Am. J. Psychol. 55:248-254, 1942.

————: The cultivation of physiological relaxation, Ann. Int. Med. 19: 965-972, 1943.

————: Direct measurements of the effects of bromides, sodium amytal and of caffeine in man, Ann. Int. Med. 21:455-468, 1944.

————: Neuromuscular controls in man: Methods of self-direction in health and in disease, Am. J. Psychol. 68:549-61, 1955.

Peterson, R. D., Beatty, C. H., and Bocek, R. M.: High energy phosphate compounds of rat diaphragm and skeletal muscle fibers, Am. J. Physiol. 200:1, 182-186, 1961.

Index

211

Edmund Jacobson, M.D.

SELF-OPERATIONS Control

A MANUAL FOR THE PATIENT—

to be used in conjunction with professional instruction in the management of anxiety and tension states.

J. B. LIPPINCOTT COMPANY

INTRODUCTION

Tension Symptoms and Complaints
Two Faces of the Same Coin

Your tension symptoms are sufficient indication that you do not know how to run your organism efficiently. However, you can learn to do this, just as you can learn to run a car. Once you have learned, you will not have to keep your mind on your muscles any more than when you walk. Control becomes a habit, second nature, and occurs almost automatically as a better way of living.

Tension symptoms in you, as in others, may include undue fatigue, poor sleep, irritability, constipation, spells of diarrhea following strain, abdominal pains, palpitation, tight feelings in the chest, poor concentration, dizziness, weakness and an extensive variety of pains and discomforts.

Do not watch symptoms. Develop skill as you would in learning to swim or to play some game. Just see what happens as you learn to save your energies! Signs of progress may appear soon, even within a few days; or there may be delay, depending upon your state and other matters. But if you practice daily, you are doing something that is basic!

Running Your Car

To run your car, you sit in the driver's seat and manipulate the ignition key, the accelerator, the gear shift or hydromatic drive, the steering wheel and the brake. These are the controls. See Figure 1 on page 2.

By manipulating the controls, you make the wheels go around at a rate and in the direction which suit your purposes. This is driving.

You yourself are a living instrument which can be run like your car, if you know how. You will be the driver, for nobody else can do it.

1

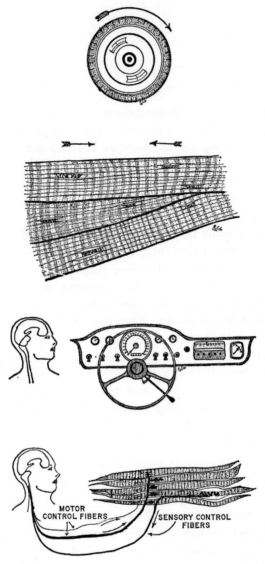

Fig. 1. You run your car by manipulating the controls on and near the dashboard, whereby you make the wheels move at the rate and in the direction you desire. Likewise, you can run yourself by going on and off with the power in the controls which lie in your muscles, whereupon your muscles contract and relax in the patterns which suit your effort-purposes.

You have no wheels, but you have the equivalent. Muscles are the equivalent. Wheels turn and can do so because they are made of hard, brittle materials. Muscles are plastic and soft, and thus they can perform in many ways far better than wheels.

Everything you do from morning till night and from night till morning is done by muscles. What muscles look like is familiar to you. Raw steak is muscle.

Muscles are made up of fibers. Each fiber is so thin that by itself it is invisible to the naked eye. Each one courses straight or round about. When fibers shorten, this is muscle contraction. You know it as "effort." When fibers lengthen, effort is discontinued. This is relaxation in the scientific sense of the word, which we shall use exclusively.

Every effort you make, then, is performed by shortening and ended by lengthening of muscle fibers.

When you think, you are making efforts, but you do not realize this. You are to learn to recognize these efforts. They include very complicated patterns of muscle tension and relaxation. Repeated practice helps, for tension signals are very slight and fleeting. You will learn to recognize them just as a telegrapher learns to recognize the sound signals of the Morse code.

What about your brain and nerves? There is no moving fiber in brain or nerves. Therefore they do not move you as wheels move the car. Certainly, your brain and nerves participate in your every effort, but they correspond, not to the wheels of your car, but to what lies under the hood. Brain and nerves are indispensible, for a child born without a brain could not move but would lie like a heap of flesh on the floor. However, your brain and your nerves are like telephone wires, not like wheels. In you, what corresponds to moving wheels are your moving muscles.

You can do many things a car cannot. You can, for example, lift your arm to comb your hair; you can talk; you can hear; you can use the camera which is your eyes. Really you have a double camera, for not only can you see what is before you, but also you can imagine what is going on elsewhere, seeing this also. In other words, you can have visual images of what is or may be going on elsewhere. While talking with one person, you often see in imagination what some other person might say or do. This is mental activity.

The automobile does not engage in mental activity. Its wheels do not enable it to think. Your muscles enable you to think. This you will discover for yourself later on.

As you learn to control the operations of your muscles, including the minute ones which always are employed when you think, you are learning self-operations control. Mind and body are one operating unit, not two. This operating unit always is based on muscle contraction.

Where are your controls? They must be where you can get at them to operate. You will find that they are in your muscles! To make this discovery, bend back your left hand. While doing this, notice the delicate sensation signal you get in the muscles in the upper surface of your left forearm. This signal will be largely absent in the right forearm, if you keep this arm at ease. Compare the two regions, so as to note the signal present in the left forearm when you are bending the left hand back, but absent on the right, when not bending.

Once more, note carefully the sensation-signal thus present on the left. This is the control we have been looking for. There are many ways to use this signal profitably for your efficiency.

Over-all View

A car has four wheels which move together and which you control when you drive. You have over 1,000 muscles which never move together when under control but which move in the most complex patterns and networks in accordance with your purposes.

In each of your muscles the controls which you can learn to operate lie inside the tiny fibers. These are in spindles so small that they can be seen only if magnified under a microscope (See Figure 1). There are thousands of controls in each muscle, yet you can learn to operate the muscles if you learn to recognize the control sensation-signals. These are present when the muscle fibers shorten. They are absent when the fibers lengthen. Their absence is what we shall call relaxation. There is no positive signal of being relaxed.

You will not need to learn how to operate each and every muscle individually, but in groups.

Chart for Learning

You are to learn how to get power on and off in groups of muscles according to what you are doing. For sleep, you want power off in all muscles directly under your control. Indeed, this is sleep in its most restful form. At any moment of daily activities, you want power on in those muscle groups needed for what you are doing but power off in those not needed. Thus you avoid waste of vital energies, avert fatigue, wear and tear and save yourself generally. We call this *differential control*.

Chart for Thorough Course

In the lying position, the order of learning (a) to distinguish the control signal in each chief muscle group and thereupon (b) to go off with the power is as follows: Left Arm: 7 days; right arm: 7 days; left leg, 10 days; right leg, 10 days; trunk, 10 days; neck, 6 days; eye-region, 12 days; visualization, 9 days; speech region, 19 days.

In the sitting position, the same order and the same duration are required.

You are to proceed from one muscle group to the following, in order of the drawings on pages 14 to 32 inclusive. Generally, you practice one tension per hour-period. You are to perform this one tension three times. As a rule this is all you do in a single hour. You do not practice several different tensions in a single hour.

Briefer Course

In a shortened course, you spend less time on each part. One way of abridgement is to perform Arm 1, Arm 2 and Arm 3 in 1 hour, instead of 3 hours. Under this regimen, for example, in one hour-period you will bend your hand back 3 times with 5-minute rests in between, then forward 3 times with 5-minute rests in between and finally go negative, relaxing the whole forearm for the last 25 minutes of the hour. Guess at the time intervals. Do not follow your watch.

Similar abridgement can be performed in practice on the legs and other parts of the body. Thus, the course can be shortened to 1/3 of the time employed for a more thorough course. However, in this as in other important tasks of life, thoroughness pays off.

Once you have learned to observe your effort tensions and to get power off where not needed in any task, you do not have to keep your mind on it, for it becomes second nature to run your organism efficiently, just as you learn to drive a car.

Read directions for Arm Practice on page 14. If you practice an hour a day, in the unabridged course your first day will be devoted exclusively to Left Arm 1. Then 14 days will be required to cover both arms.

General Plan for Learning

The general plan for learning will be illustrated in the following directions for your first period. Read the directions and look at the drawing for Left Arm 1 on page 14. You will find 8 instructions for steps to be followed *consecutively* during the hour-period. You are to take 8 similar steps in Period No. 2, except that in Period 2 you are to bend the left hand forward instead of backwards.

The same eight instructions will apply during every period of the entire course, except that the act performed will vary with the number of the period, as shown by the drawings.

This rule will not hold for every third time you practice, for in this hour you should omit tensing altogether. Simply relax only. In this way you will avoid forming the wrong habit of tensing a part before you begin to relax it. For examples, note that in Left Arm Period 3 and Period 6 you are not to tense at all.

Your First Period

To make a beginning, read the instructions for Left Arm 1 on page 14. Also, read what is said below on pages 7 to 11 which applies to all periods of practice. Then lie down on a couch or bed alone in a room with doors closed. Avoid being called during the hour.*

Let your arms rest at your sides, your hands a little away from your body, and do not cross your legs. Leave your eyes open for 3 or 4 minutes and then close them gradually. Guess at the time; do not look at any clock or watch.

Bend Left Hand Back. Why?

When your eyes have remained closed for an estimated 3 or 4 minutes more, bend back your left hand at the wrist steadily, without fluctuation. Do not seesaw. While doing so, with care you can note a vague misty sensation in the upper surface of your left forearm. You may call it "tightness." This is the signal of tension, the control, which you are to learn to recognize, just as a telegrapher must learn to recognize sound-signals.

Avoid Prolonged Attention to Tension Signals

Do not give prolonged attention to the control signal. Some people mistakenly keep watching their tension signals during the entire hour of practice. Thereby they do not really go negative, for really they are keeping their eyes continually busy in the act of attention to muscle signals and this triggers tension over their entire musculature.

Control Signal vs. Strain Signal

Distinguish the signal of tension from the stronger signal of *strain* at the wrist. The strain signal in the wrist stands out more. However, you can not run yourself by strains, any more

---

* Do not interrupt the practice to read. However, after your first hour of practice, read the instructions mentioned once again, for then they will mean more to you.

than a motor car can be driven by strains on the motor. What is important for running yourself is the control signal in and from the muscle. It informs you, however grossly, when and where you are expending effort-energy. Besides, the controls are important if you want to learn self-engineering—just as important as are the control devices on the dashboard of your car if you want to drive it.

Repetition Required

Once more, then, bend your left hand back in order to observe the control sensation again. This is going on with the power exactly where you note the muscle signal, which is where you are performing work.

No Switch and No Effort to Relax

To go off requires no turning of a switch, for there is no switch. It is far simpler than when you switch off the electric light. Then work is required to move the switch (work is forces times distance).

However, no work is required to go off with the power in your forearm. All you need to do is to *discontinue* working there. No effort is required. An effort to relax is failure to relax. Untrained people often fail to relax because they work to relax.

To tense requires continuous effort-work so long as tensing is maintained. The moment you discontinue tensing (without effort to do so) you relax. This is *power off*, going negative. All you need to do is to discontinue working. It is simple and easy.

Many people ask, "What shall I think about when I lie down?" Please read the following answer more than once: You are not told to think and you are not told to make your mind a blank! During Practice Period 1 and during following practice periods, if you find yourself thinking about yourself, your practice or anything else, go off with the power in the muscle regions on which you are now practicing or have practiced in foregoing periods. If the thinking recurs, go negative again, no matter how often.

Avoid Autosuggestion and Hypnosis

Do not tell yourself in words, "This will make me feel fine!" If, at the close of any practice period you are pleased and tell yourself, "I felt as if floating!", the truth is that you have not really relaxed but instead have engaged in autosuggestive fantasy. Such procedures render you dependent on words or on hypnotists. In self-engineering, autosuggestion and hypnosis have no place whatsoever. Therefore, read the directions again and follow them carefully.

Control Progresses

In practicing going negative in any muscle, go negative likewise in the parts on which you have practiced in preceding periods.

Residual Tension

As you will find, tension, like a conflagration, does not go to zero readily. When anybody lies down, including your cat or dog, measurements show that tension does not subside to zero as a rule. On the contrary, some tension tends to persist unnecessarily in every muscle. This is called *residual tension.* Because residual tension tends to be with you always, you need have no concern that our practices will make you too relaxed. No one ever learns to draw a perfect circle or to play golf perfectly and no one ever learns to relax perfectly. Whatever the skill you develop in tension control, there will always remain a great gap between the point you reach and perfection. Have no fear that tension control ever will make you lazy!

In Practice Period 7, after relaxing the entire left arm for about 5 minutes with eyes closed, begin to stiffen the entire left arm without moving even a finger. Proceed to stiffen very gradually, continuously (without sudden increments) increasing the rigidity. This will not be what we want until you have learned to take several minutes to perform the increase uniformly.

Do not stiffen your arm to the point of extreme effort but only in moderation. When the arm has very gradually become moderately tense or rigid, begin to go negative very, very slowly and gradually. The instruction is: Whatever you have done up to this point in stiffening your arm, begin now to do it a very little less and gradually less, less and less, even up to and beyond the point where the arm appears to you to be quite relaxed, i.e., perfectly free from control signal. You can safely assume that even at this point you are still engaging at least a little in residual tensing. Accordingly, whatever you have been doing negatively up to this point, continue on negatively further and further for another 10 or 15 minutes. But make no effort to hold still or to relax.

Analogous progressive relaxation instructions apply to Period 14, Right Arm, Period 10, Left Leg, and so on.

Tension Control During Hours of Daily Activity

To some extent, your gains in tension control from practice lying down will be transferred into your daily habits at work and at play. This will occur automatically. As you learn, it becomes second nature. However, while fully relaxed muscles are not needed during any occupation (indeed would render such activity impossible), some degree of control can improve your efficiency during any type of occupation. Watch yourself occasionally, however briefly, to see if you are excessively vigorous even in the tensions needed to carry out your purposes. Do you grasp your pen or pencil very tightly when you write? Do you talk too loudly or too long from overtension? Are your eyes always looking? These tensions are called *primary* because they are needed. However, if they are over-vigorous, you are paying too big a price in energy reserves. You should relax these tensions but only partially, because you need them for your job or pleasure. Do you doodle? If so, this is tension called *secondary* because it is not needed. Any secondary tension has nuisance value only and should be relaxed completely.

Need To Observe Faintest Control Signal

You are to learn to recognize very faint control signals. Why? It is important because you have built-in equipment for performing major efforts based on faint controls. To sign a binding contract requires little effort energy, notwithstanding that the consequences may affect your entire subsequent fortunes and existence. Your tensions in signing a contract or engaging in any other significant effort-pattern evidently do not depend on their intensity for the importance of their consequences. Like the signals of the telegrapher's keys, it is the pattern rather than the strength of signals which conveys the significance.

In a word, self-operations control is the science for living which depends on recognizing and employing the faintest effort-signals in the interest of practical welfare.

If You Fall Asleep

You are not requested to try to go to sleep during your practice periods or to try to stay awake, but, if you should fall asleep as you go negative, there is no objection.

VISUALIZATION AND SPEECH

Follow the directions on visualization on page 26 and on subsequent days those on speech on pages 27 to 29 inclusive. To learn the significance of these practices and how they can help you to save your mental energies, read the section on pages 11 to 12 entitled Control of Mind. It is well to read this section more than once, not only before you begin the visualization practice, but also again afterwards. Also, you might profitably read this section repeatedly before and after the days devoted to attaining skill in observing and controlling tensions of the speech muscles.

CONTROL OF MIND

When you think or imagine or engage in any other form of mental activity, your brain is active, but to no greater extent than when you engage in any so-called physical activity, such as golf. Without a brain you could not think, but neither could you play golf. At no time do you feel your brain working; neither do you ever have tension signals in the brain. As you learn to recognize tensions, you will find them chiefly in the eyes and speech regions on thinking, but not in the brain.

You can learn to control your thinking and emotions to a useful extent because these mental activities occur only if and when you tense your eye and speech muscles. However, you may use also every other muscle in your body in thinking and in emotion, depending on the patterns which correspond to your endeavors.

Electrical measurements show, for instance, that people use their arm muscles often in imagination.

Close your eyes and think about any matter. If skilled, you will notice (1) visual pictures, called images, but also (2) eye tensions to look at what you see in imagination. In thinking, also, you are likely to use your speech apparatus to form words, but these are not spoken aloud. Electrical measurements disclose that you use the same muscles as you use in saying the same words aloud.

However, you should discover for yourself (on following the instructions for visualization and for speech on pp. 26 to 29 inclusive), that the tension signals and the image signals are delicate, fleeting and greatly abbreviated. Otherwise, in visual imagination you look at the objects you think about, turning your eyes in the same way as if you were looking at real objects.

Thus, imagination is a shorthand, a telescopic reproduction in which you use your muscles just as you do in reality when you see objects or persons and speak aloud. However, in mental activity the tensions are miniscule. As said above, you will find that all other muscles may and do participate in some of your tension-image patterns.

When you engage in any mental or physical effort, the brain and the muscles act approximately simultaneously. That the brain has an idea first which later is expressed in the muscles is an incorrect view for which no evidence ever was presented, although many people held it and still do.

When Muscle Power Is Off

At any moment if the muscles either of the arms or legs or trunk are really relaxed approximately to zero tension, the mind is thereby quieted. Why? Because in thinking or emotion, tensions in the parts mentioned participate. They are the actors in any and every play of the mind. Without them participating, the mind is vacant.

Understanding this will enable you to apprehend why "the mind relaxes" when the limbs or trunk or any other larger section of the body relaxes. However, remember that for this the tension-signals must be reduced to zero or nearly so. If the reduction falls short, leaving tension signals of a diminished but sufficient order, then, as when the telegrapher's signals are still faintly present, the messages are still there and the mind keeps on working. See Figure 2, below.

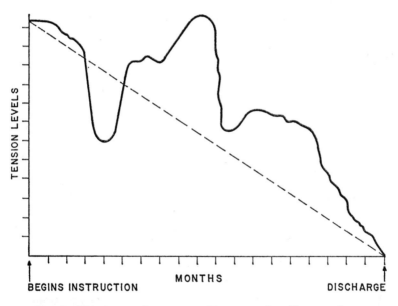

Fig. 2. This is one of many possible curves that illustrate that you should not expect uninterrupted improvement. The course of improvement never runs smooth but, generally, is marked by ups and downs. There will be times of discouragement and relapse but these offer valuable opportunities to learn how to meet difficult moments.

ARM PRACTICE

In each hour-practice period, follow the appropriate photograph, performing the tension indicated 3 times at intervals of several minutes. These are NOT exercises. Interest yourself in becoming familiar with the control sensation in each part so that you can learn really to run yourself properly relaxed under all conditions.

Periods	Left Arm	Periods	Right Arm
1.	Bend hand back.	8.	Bend hand back.
2.	Bend hand forward.	9.	Bend hand forward.
3.	Relax only.	10.	Relax only.
4.	Bend at elbow.	11.	Bend at elbow.
5.	Press wrist down on books.	12.	Press wrist down on books.
6.	Relax only.	13.	Relax only.
7.	Progressive tension and relaxation of whole	14.	Progressive tension and relaxation of whole arm

Arm 1   Lying

Period No. 1

Select a quiet room, free from intruders and phone calls.

1. Lying on your back with arms at sides, leave eyes open 3 to 4 minutes.

2. Gradually close eyes and keep them closed entire hour.

3. After 3 to 4 minutes with eyes closed, bend left hand back (see photograph), observing the control sensation 1 to 2 minutes and how it differs from the strains in the wrist and in the lower portion of the forearm.

4. Go negative for 3 to 4 minutes.

5. Again bend left hand back and observe as previously.

6. Once more go negative 3 to 4 minutes.

7. Bend left hand back a third and last time, observing the control sensation 1 to 2 minutes.

8. Finally go negative for remainder of hour.

Arm 1: Lying
Bend hand back. (Felt in back upper part of forearm)

Arm 2: Lying
Bend hand forward. (Felt in front of forearm)

Arm 3   Lying
PERIOD No. 3

Lie quietly on back as previously, arms at sides. In this *and in all subsequent periods lying down,* leave eyes open several minutes, then gradually close them and *keep closed* for entire hour. Throughout this period go negative only: Do not bend, extend or stiffen the arm; but if you should do so, awaredly or unawaredly, note the slight control sensation which will thereupon appear in the left arm and go negative there at once.

Do not tense to relax.

In General

Period No. 3 is called a zero period.

Hereafter, every third period is to be a zero period. In other practice periods, specialize on one tension only, performing the three times.

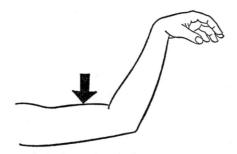

Arm 4: Lying
Bend arm at elbow, about 35°. (Felt in
biceps, front of upper arm)

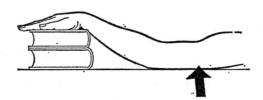

Arm 5: Lying
Press wrist down against books. (Felt
in back part of upper arm)

LEG PRACTICE   Lying

In each daily practice period, follow the appropriate photograph, performing the tension indicated 3 times at intervals of several minutes. These are *NOT* exercises. Interest yourself in becoming familiar with the control sensation in each part so that you can learn really to run yourself properly relaxed under all conditions.

DAY	LEFT LEG	DAY	RIGHT LEG
1.	Bend foot up.	11.	Bend foot up.
2.	Bend foot down.	12.	Bend foot down.
3.	Relax only.	13.	Relax only.
4.	Raise foot.	14.	Raise foot.
5.	Bend at knee.	15.	Bend at knee.
6.	Relax only.	16.	Relax only.
7.	Raise knee.	17.	Raise knee.
8.	Press lower thigh down.	18.	Press lower thigh down.
9.	Relax entire left leg.	19.	Relax entire right knee.
10.	Progressive tension and relaxation of entire left leg.	20.	Progressive tension and relaxation of entire right leg.

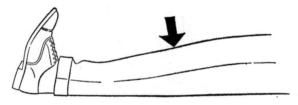

Leg 1: Lying
Bend foot up. (Felt along front of lower leg)

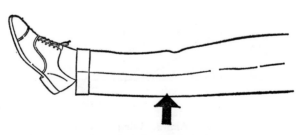

Leg 2: Lying
Extend foot. (Felt in calf)

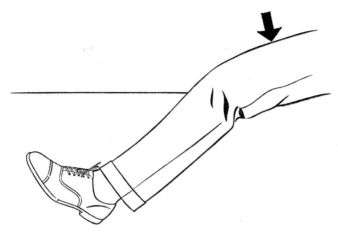

Leg 4: Lying
Raise foot and leg. (Felt in front part
of thigh)

Leg 5: Lying
Bend leg at knee. (Felt along back of
thigh)

Leg 7: Lying
Raise knee, bending at hip. (Felt in muscles deep in abdomen, toward back, near hip)

Leg 8: Lying
Press lower thigh against books. (Felt in buttocks)

TRUNK PRACTICE

In each daily practice period, follow the appropriate photograph, performing the tension indicated 3 times at intervals of several minutes. These are *NOT* exercises. Interest yourself in becoming familiar with the control sensation in each part so that you can learn really to run yourself properly relaxed under all conditions.

DAY   TRUNK
1.   Pull in abdomen.
2.   Arch back slightly.
3.   Relax abdomen, back and legs.
4.   Observe during a deeper breath.
5.   Bend shoulders back.
6.   Relax only.
7.   Left arm forward and inward.
8.   Right arm forward and inward.
9.   Relax only.
10.   Elevate shoulders.

Trunk 1: Lying
Pull in abdomen. (Felt faintly all over abdomen)

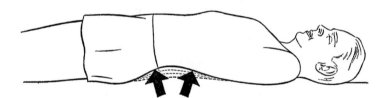

Trunk 2: Lying
Arch the back. (Felt definitely along both sides of the spine)

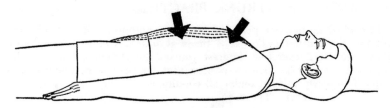

Trunk 4: Lying
Observe during a deeper breath. (Very
faint diffuse tenseness felt all over chest)

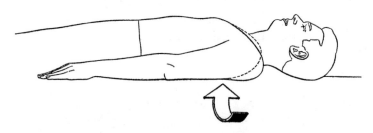

Trunk 5: Lying
Bend shoulders back. (Felt in back,
between shoulder blades)

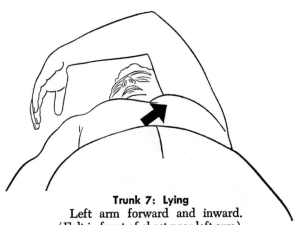

Trunk 7: Lying
Left arm forward and inward.
(Felt in front of chest near left arm)

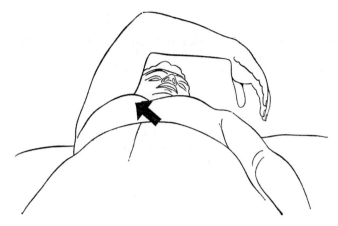

Trunk 8: Lying
Right arm forward and inward. (Felt
in front of chest on right)

Trunk 10: Lying
Elevate shoulders. (Felt along top of
shoulders and in sides of neck)

NECK PRACTICE   Lying

In each daily practice period, follow the appropriate photograph, performing the tension indicated 3 times at intervals of several minutes. These are *NOT* exercises. Interest yourself in becoming familiar with the control sensation in each part so that you can learn really to run yourself properly relaxed under all conditions.

Day	Neck, Lying
1.	Bend head back.
2.	Bend chin toward chest.
3.	Relax only.
4.	Bend head left.
5.	Bend head right.
6.	Relax only.

Neck 1: Lying
Bend head back. (Felt in back of neck, perhaps below, in back)

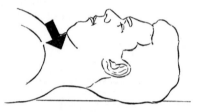

Neck 2: Lying
Bend chin down. (Felt in sides of neck)

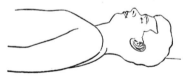

Neck 3: Lying
Relax only.

Neck 4: Lying
Bend head left. (Felt in left side of neck)

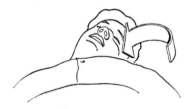

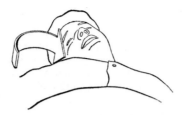

Neck 5: Lying
Bend head right. (Felt
in right side of neck)

Neck 6: Lying
Relax only.

EYE REGION PRACTICE

In each daily practice period, follow the appropriate photograph, performing the tension indicated 3 times at intervals of several minutes. These are *NOT* exercises. Interest yourself in becoming familiar with the control sensation in each part so that you can learn really to run yourself properly relaxed under all conditions.

DAY	EYE REGION
1.	Wrinkle forehead.
2.	Frown.
3.	Relax only.
4.	Close eyelids tightly.
5.	Look left with lids closed.
6.	Relax only.
7.	Look right with lids closed.
8.	Look up.
9.	Relax only.
10.	Look downward with lids closed.
11.	Look forward with lids closed.
12.	Relax only.

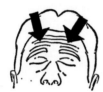

Eye Region 1: Lying
Wrinkle forehead. (Felt diffusely over entire forehead)

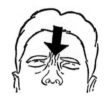

Eye Region 2: Lying
Frown. (Felt distinctly between eyes)

Eye Region 4: Lying
Close eyelids tightly. (Felt all over eyelids)

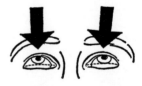

Eye Region 5: Lying
Look up (eyelids closed). (Felt in eyeball muscles at top; tensions change rapidly as eyes move)

Eye Region 7: Lying
Look right (eyelids closed). (Felt in eyeball muscles, right; note static and moving tensions)

Eye Region 8: Lying
Look left (eyelids closed). (Felt in eyeball muscles, left)

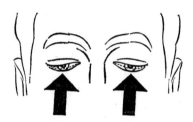

Eye Region 10: Lying
Look down (eyelids closed). (Felt in eyeball muscles, below)

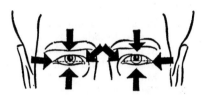

Eye Region 11: Lying
Look forward (eyelids closed). (Felt in muscles all around eyeballs)

VISUALIZATION PRACTICE
With lids open
With lids closed

In each daily practice period, follow the appropriate photograph, performing the tension indicated 3 times at intervals of several minutes. These are *NOT* exercises. Interest yourself in becoming familiar with the control sensation in each part so that you can learn really to run yourself properly relaxed under all conditions.

DAY	VISUALIZATION	DAY	VISUALIZATION
1.	Imagine pen moving side to side.	4.	Bird flying from tree to tree. Bird still.
	Make it go very slowly.	5.	Ball rolling on ground.
	Make it stand still.		Ball still.
	Make it go very fast.		Eiffel tower.
2.	Skyrocket train passing quickly.	6.	Relax only.
	Man walking by.	7.	Rabbit on road.
3.	Relax eyes to zero.		Head of pin.
		8.	President of U. S.
		9.	Relax only.

SPEECH REGION PRACTICE

In each daily practice period, follow the appropriate photograph, performing the tension indicated 3 times at intervals of several minutes. These are *NOT* exercises. Interest yourself in becoming familiar with the control sensation in each part so that you can learn really to run yourself properly relaxed under all conditions.

DAY

1. Close jaws somewhat firmly.
2. Open jaws.
3. Relax only.
4. Show teeth (as if smiling).
5. Pout.
6. Relax only.
7. Push tongue forward against teeth.
8. Pull tongue backward.
9. Relax only.
10. Count to 10.
11. Count half as loudly.
12. Relax only.

DAY

13. Count very faintly.
14. Count imperceptibly.
15. Relax only.
16. Imagine that you are counting.
17. Imagine you are saying alphabet.
18. Relax only.
19. Imagine saying name three times.
    Address three times.
    Name of President three times.

Speech Region 1: Lying
Close jaws rather firmly. (Felt at back of lower jaw and in temples)

Speech Region 2: Lying
Open jaws. (Felt in sides of lower jaw and neck)

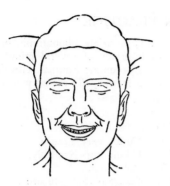

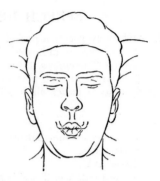

Speech Region 4: Lying
Show teeth (as if smiling). (Felt in cheeks)

Speech Region 5: Lying
Pout. (Felt in and around lips)

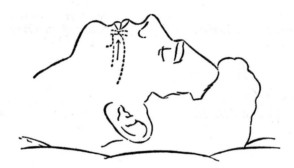

Speech Region 7: Lying
Push tongue against teeth. (Felt in tongue)

Speech Region 8: Lying
Pull tongue backwards. (Felt in tongue and floor of mouth)

Speech Region 10: Lying
Count to 10. (Felt
in cheeks, lips,
tongue, jaw muscles,
throat, chest and,
perhaps, abdomen)

Arm 1: Sitting
Bend hand back. (Felt in
back part of forearm)

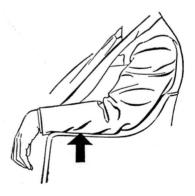

Arm 2: Sitting
Bend hand down. (Felt in
front part of forearm)

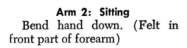

Arm 4: Sitting
Bend arm at elbow. (Felt in biceps, front of upper arm)

Arm 5: Sitting
Press wrist down against arm of chair. (Felt in back, upper arm)

Leg 1: Sitting
Bend foot up. (Felt along front of lower leg)

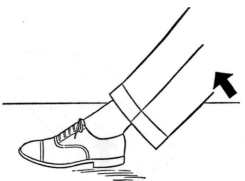

Leg 2: Sitting
Press toe end of foot down. (Felt in calf)

Leg 4: Sitting
Raise foot without moving
thigh. (Felt in front of thigh)

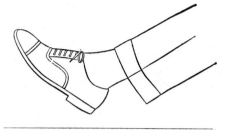

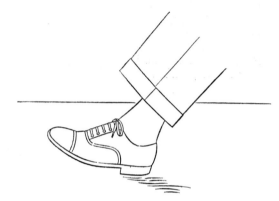

Leg 5: Sitting
Pull heel back
without moving
thigh. (Felt along
back of thigh)

Leg 7: Sitting
Press down whole
foot. (Felt in buttocks)

Leg 8: Sitting
Raise knee while foot
hangs limply. (Felt in
psoas muscles deep in ab-
domen, toward back)

NECK PRACTICE   Sitting

In each daily practice period, follow the appropriate photograph, performing the tension indicated 3 times at intervals of several minutes. These are *NOT* exercises. Interest yourself in becoming familiar with the control sensation in each part so that you can learn really to run yourself properly relaxed under all conditions.

DAY   NECK, SITTING
1.   Bend head back slightly.
2.   Bend chin toward chest.
3.   Relax only.
4.   Bend head right.
5.   Bend head left.
6.   Relax only.
7.   Head erect. Relax neck
      as far as possible.